Word Game

Increase Vocabulary through Fun and

Challenging Games and Puzzles!

Grades 3–4

Credits

Author: Mary Newmaster

Production: Quack & Company, Inc.

Illustrations: Sherry Neidigh

Cover Design: Peggy Jackson

This book has been correlated to state, national, and Canadian provincial standards. Visit *www.carsondellosa.com* to search for and view its correlations to your standards.

ISBN 0-88724-956-6

Table of Contents

Introduction

Word Games is a fun way for students to increase their vocabularies, sharpen their reading skills, and learn some fascinating facts! This book is filled with an exciting variety of games and puzzles that students will enjoy completing. The book features interesting events which occur during the year. The activities complement the events and include specific skills to enhance vocabulary development.

Solving crossword puzzles and word searches, completing analogies, and unscrambling words are just a few of the stimulating types of word-based activities students complete in this book. All words are grade-appropriate, and the activities are sure to improve a variety of language skills.

Students will be fascinated by the information featured in the activities. They will learn about special annual events, such as National Pizza Month in October and Save a Spider Day on March 14. The students will also learn about important historical events, such as the discovery of the South Pole and the opening of the first gas station. The fun, fact-filled activities are sure to motivate them to complete every page.

Whether you want to improve students' vocabulary skills or just provide them with meaningful and stimulating word-based activities, *Word Games* is sure to delight and captivate all who complete its pages.

Labor
Day

Name _____

Celebrate Work

Labor Day honors working people. It is celebrated on the first Monday in September throughout the United States, Puerto Rico, and Canada.

To find out what is important to every occupation, unscramble each occupation on the left. Use the pictures as clues. Then, write the letter from each box in order on the blanks below.

1. hcef   ___ ☐ ___ ___

2. tsdneit   ☐ ___ ___ ___ ___ ___ ___

3. ruahot   ___ ___ ☐ ___ ___ ___

4. oenpmclai   ___ ___ ___ ___ ☐ ___ ___ ___ ___

5. atrchee   ___ ___ ☐ ___ ___ ___ ___

6. tasitr   ___ ___ ___ ___ ☐ ___

7. greethiriff   ___ ☐ ___ ___ ___ ___ ___ ___ ___ ___ ___

8. poilt   ___ ___ ___ ☐ ___

9. usner   ☐ ___ ___ ___ ___

___ ___ ___ ___ ___ ___ ___ ___ ___

Name _____

Ice Cream Treat

In September of 1903, Italo Marchiony applied for a patent for the ice cream cone. Ice cream cones were served the following year at the 1904 World's Fair in St. Louis, Missouri.

Using the definition, write a five-letter word with the vowel sound listed on the ice cream. Then, subtract one letter from the word to make a four-letter word with the same vowel sound. Continue until only the vowel is left.

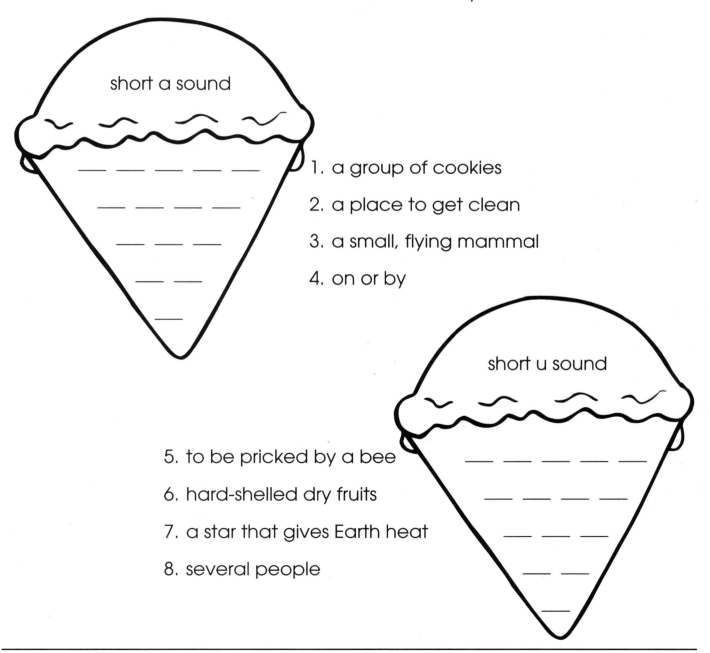

short a sound

1. a group of cookies

2. a place to get clean

3. a small, flying mammal

4. on or by

5. to be pricked by a bee

6. hard-shelled dry fruits

7. a star that gives Earth heat

8. several people

short u sound

Name _____

Let's Eat Healthy!

To promote good eating habits, a week is spent in September to help encourage every person to eat five servings of fruits and vegetables every day. Fruits and vegetables provide our bodies with important vitamins and minerals.

Write the fruits and vegetables from the Word Bank in the puzzle. Then, unscramble the circled letters to answer the question below.

Word Bank

apple	kiwi	pear
banana	lemon	spinach
beet	onion	zucchini
celery	orange	

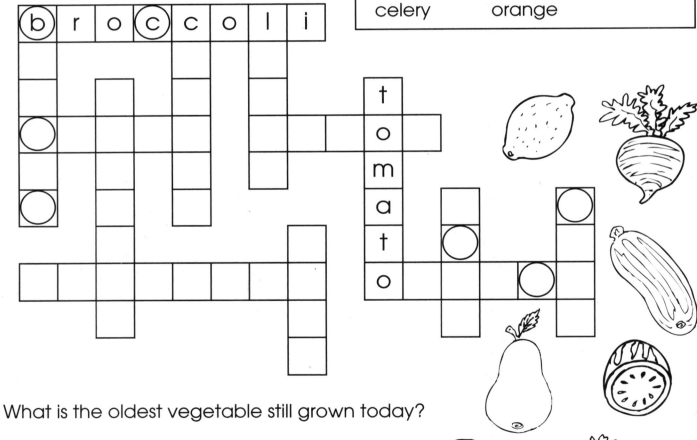

b r o c c o l i

t o m a t o

What is the oldest vegetable still grown today?

___ ___ ___ ___ ___ ___ ___

It has been grown for over 4,000 years!

Name _____

A Giant Birthday

September 13 is Roald Dahl's birthday. This author has written many popular children's books including *Charlie and the Chocolate Factory*.

To find out the title of another book written by Roald Dahl, write a five-letter word with a long e sound for each definition. Then, write the shaded letters in order on the blanks below to discover the title.

1. denim pants

2. metric linear measurement

3. more than one goose

4. not dirty

5. a thought while sleeping

6. used for chewing

7. a taste with lots of sugar

8. to go along with another's idea

9. thoughts

10. a female ruler

11. one type of Native American home

12. to exit

13. a sandy shore

__ __ __ __ __ __ __   __ __ __ __   __ __   __ __ __ __ __ __   __ __ __ __

Name _____

Follow the Path

On September 16, 1602, the Mayflower left Plymouth, England, for America. This ship carried 102 passengers across the Atlantic Ocean.

To sail the ship below, write the word for each definition. The last letter of each word is the first letter of the next word.

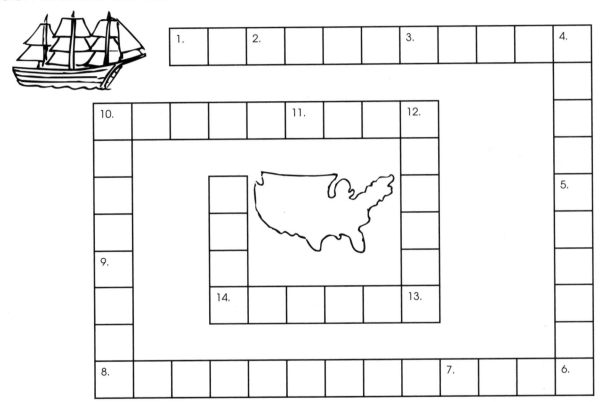

1. a short rest

2. a device used to call someone

3. the joint in the middle of an arm

4. a wheeled cart

5. not very wide

6. a long, thin animal with no legs or backbone

7. a small metric measurement

8. a law

9. to go into a building

10. an area of a country

11. a place a bird may live

12. a covered passage

13. very small

14. simple

Name _____

Almost the Same

The autumnal equinox is one of two days during the year when the sun is directly above the equator. On these two days, day and night are nearly the same length everywhere on Earth.

Night and *knight* are homophones because they sound the same but are spelled differently. Circle the homophone in the puzzle for each word in the Word Bank. Words will go across, up, down, and diagonally.

Word Bank

dear
fairy
hall
heard
made
no
not
pail
pain
peace
pour
reed
some
sore
sun
wood

```
t  e  l  w  a  d  g  s  j  n
m  n  s  o  p  k  n  o  t  o
k  a  p  u  l  a  m  a  f  s
n  p  i  l  t  h  l  r  e  u
o  c  e  d  v  a  h  e  r  d
w  o  c  w  s  u  m  p  r  a
f  d  e  e  r  l  n  o  y  q
p  m  f  r  e  a  d  o  d  e
b  r  e  a  t  m  c  r  k  j
```

Name _____

Stamp and Mail

The first United States Postmaster General was appointed in September of 1789. At that time, there were only 75 post offices. Today, almost 570 million pieces of mail are delivered daily.

Use the definitions and the letters in *stamp* and *mail* to complete each puzzle.

s				
	t			
		a		
			m	
				p

1. very clever

2. a platform

3. garbage

4. a picture border

5. to clean a floor

m			
	a		
		i	
			l

6. turn into liquid

7. statement that is true

8. move in water

9. not fake

10

Name _____

Female Justices

On September 25, 1981, Sandra Day O'Connor became the first female justice of the United States Supreme Court. Twelve years later, another woman was appointed to this court.

To find out the name of the second female Supreme Court justice, write a verb in the boxes for each definition. To spell her name, write the letters from the bolded boxes in order on the lines at the bottom of the page.

1. to move quickly

2. to move forward, a shove

3. to get a hold of something that is moving

4. to make a sound like a bird

5. to run slowly

6. to hit with a foot

7. to sleep for a short time

8. to sense an odor

9. to take away in math

10. to hold someone tightly

11. to weep

12. to make sounds with musical tones

_____ Bader _____

Library Card Sign-Up Month

Name _____

Get Your Card Here!

September is library card sign-up month. In the United States, there are 15,000 public libraries. One of the first public libraries in the United States was started in 1833 in Peterborough, New Hampshire.

Complete the crossword puzzle using words about a library.

Across

2. the science that deals with the Earth and life on it

4. a building with many books

6. the study of the past

7. information about an event or subject

8. to learn by reading about something

10. open for all people

11. pages from books are made from this

Down

1. a daily or weekly publication

5. a ledge to place books

3. a book of maps

9. making little noise

Name _____

It's a Home Run!

On October 1, 1961, Roger Maris, a New York Yankee, hit his 61st home run of the season to break Babe Ruth's home run record. Another record-breaking home-run slugger celebrates his birthday on this day.

To find out who he is, complete the puzzle. Unscramble each word on the left. Each word includes the letters *B*, *A*, and *T*. Use the pictures as clues. Then, write the letter from each box in order on the lines below to learn the home run slugger's name.

1. batemens ___ ___ ___ [ ] ___ ___ ___ ___

2. batsl ___ ___ [ ] ___ ___

3. batibr [ ] ___ ___ ___ ___ ___

4. batkes ___ ___ ___ [ ] ___ ___

5. batamoste ___ ___ ___ ___ [ ] ___ ___ ___ ___

6. bathc ___ ___ [ ] ___ ___

7. batngti ___ ___ ___ ___ ___ ___ [ ]

8. batseektsaw [ ] ___ ___ ___ ___ ___ ___ ___ ___ ___

9. bati ___ ___ [ ] ___

10. bathre ___ [ ] [ ] ___ ___ ___

___ ___ ___ ___ ___ ___ ___ ___ ___ ___

Dessert Day

Name _____

Sweet Treats

What is your favorite dessert? Double your pleasure with two desserts in October to celebrate National Dessert Month.

Double your fun by completing the crossword puzzle with words containing double letters. Use the clues from each sentence to help you.

Across

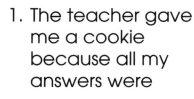

1. The teacher gave me a cookie because all my answers were _____.

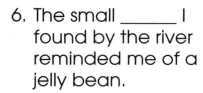

5. I won a treat when I shot the _____ in the center of the target.

6. The small _____ I found by the river reminded me of a jelly bean.

8. We walked across the _____ ice to get some hot chocolate.

9. The ice cream truck was too wide for the _____ tunnel.

10. The car was completely covered with snow because of the _____ .

Down

1. The mouse nibbled on the _____.

2. The _____ hopped through the garden looking for a carrot.

3. We need to _____ the street to get to the bakery.

4. I want to _____ every bite of that chocolate cake.

Across the Atlantic

On October 12, 1492, after traveling across the Atlantic Ocean from Spain, Christopher Columbus landed on an island in the West Indies.

To find out what Columbus named the island, solve the puzzle. Use each clue to write a word about Columbus's expedition. The first letter for each word has been given. Then write the circled letters in order on the blanks below to learn the island's name.

1. the land next to the sea

2. a person who works on a boat

3. a large body of salt water

4. a measurement used to tell the distance between two cities

5. a person who travels

6. an exciting experience

7. to declare one's own

8. to give one thing in return for something else

9. a course used for traveling

10. to investigate a new place

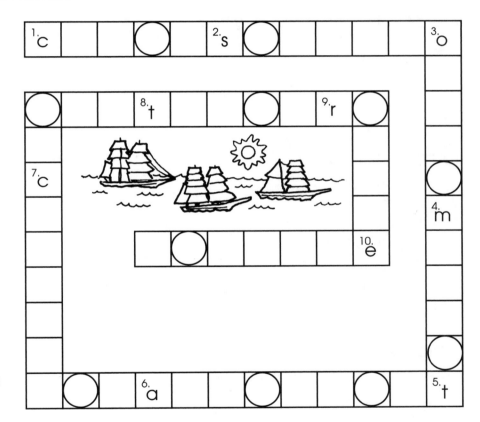

___ ___ ___ ___ ___ ___ ___ ___

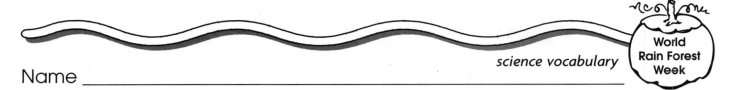

Name _____

Rain Forest Adventure

A week is spent in mid-October to raise awareness of the world's rain forests. Rain forests are home to half of the world's plant and animal species.

Take a journey into a rain forest. Use the code to fill in the letters of each missing word.

To celebrate World Rain Forest Week, you are about to take an imaginary

journey through a rain forest. As you step onto the ___ ___ ___ ___

forest floor, you immediately hear ___ ___ ___ ___ ___ ___ ___ buzzing and

___ ___ ___ ___ ___ screeching. A toad hops across the forest's carpet

which is made of ___ ___ ___ ___, leaves, and branches. Growing from the

___ ___ ___ ___ of a tree is a beautiful ___ ___ ___ ___ ___ ___.

You continue to walk through the ___ ___ ___ ___ ___ forest. The

___ ___ ___ ___ ___ ___ ___ ___ ___ ___ ___ is comfortable, but the air

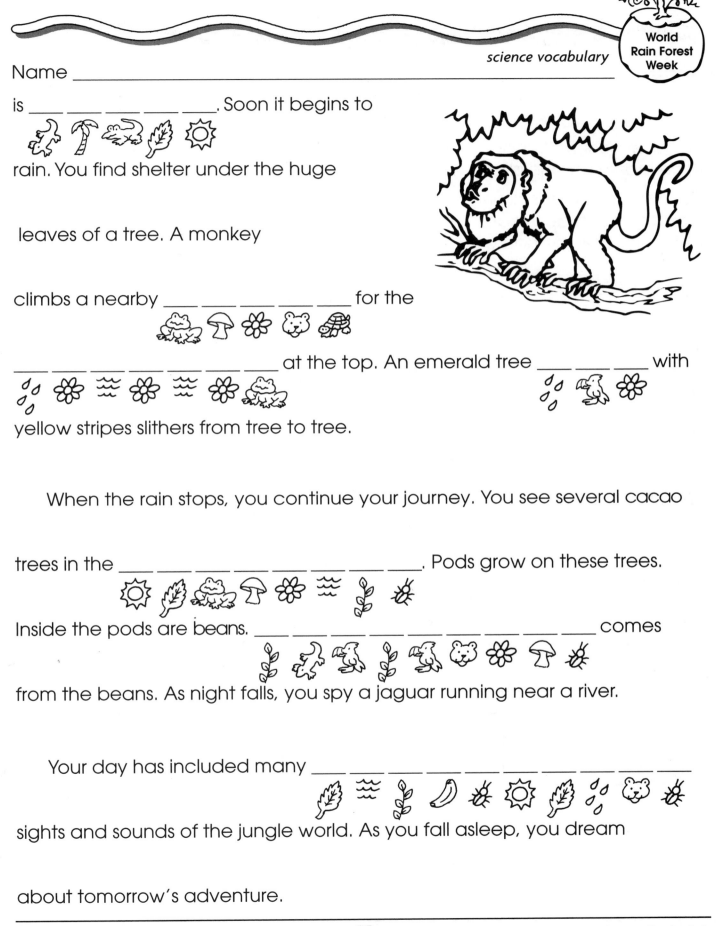

Name _____

is ___ ___ ___ ___ ___. Soon it begins to

rain. You find shelter under the huge

leaves of a tree. A monkey

climbs a nearby ___ ___ ___ ___ ___ for the

___ ___ ___ ___ ___ ___ ___ at the top. An emerald tree ___ ___ ___ with

yellow stripes slithers from tree to tree.

When the rain stops, you continue your journey. You see several cacao

trees in the ___ ___ ___ ___ ___ ___ ___ ___. Pods grow on these trees.

Inside the pods are beans. ___ ___ ___ ___ ___ ___ ___ ___ ___ comes

from the beans. As night falls, you spy a jaguar running near a river.

Your day has included many ___ ___ ___ ___ ___ ___ ___ ___ ___ ___

sights and sounds of the jungle world. As you fall asleep, you dream

about tomorrow's adventure.

Name _____

Look It Up

October 16 is Dictionary Day. This special day celebrates the birthday of the American who published a small school dictionary in 1806.

To find out this American's name, complete the puzzle. Write a two-syllable word for each definition. Then, write the shaded letters in order on the blanks below to spell the name.

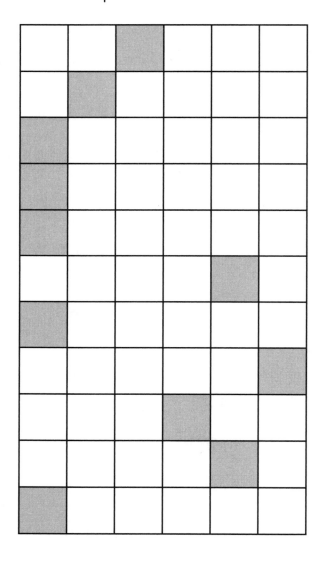

1. slender part attached to a hand

2. paper money unit

3. not present

4. to be kept out of sight

5. an opening in a wall

6. known only to oneself

7. a long struggle or combat

8. where clowns perform

9. a person who writes

10. the season after spring

11. a break time during school

___ ___ ___ ___ ___   ___ ___ ___ ___ ___ ___ ___

Name _____

Rhyme Time

Black Poetry Day is celebrated in mid-October. Alice Walker and Gwendolyn Brooks are two popular African-American poets.

To find out the name of another popular African-American poet, think of two words that rhyme for each definition. For example, a noisy mob would be a loud crowd. Then, use the number code to spell the poet's name on the blanks below.

1. a comical rabbit   __ __ __ __ __   __ __ __ __
                                                    3

2. an amusing town   __ __ __ __   __ __ __
                              6

3. a solid bacteria   __ __ __ __   __ __ __ __
                                            11

4. an outstanding ice shoe   __ __ __ __   __ __ __ __
                              4   5

5. pleasant rodents   __ __ __ __   __ __ __ __
                        8

6. a nutty flower   __ __ __ __   __ __ __ __ __
                                                14

7. a pretty salamander   __ __ __ __   __ __ __ __
                              10

8. a five-cent cucumber   __ __ __ __ __   __ __ __ __ __
                                                        13

9. a fake horse   __ __ __ __   __ __ __ __
                        12

10. a happy evergreen shrub   __ __ __ __   __ __ __ __
                              7   9

11. to take a dinner   __ __ __ __ __   __ __ __ __
                                    2   1

__ __ __ __ __ __ __ __   __ __ __ __ __ __
1 2 3 4 5 6 7 8   9 10 11 12 13 14

Name _____

Pizza Party

October is National Pizza Month. Raffaele Esposito, an Italian baker, invented pizza margherita in 1889. He created a pie with the same colors as the Italian flag.

Use the pictures and the letters in *dough* and *cheese* as clues to complete each puzzle.

Name _____

Computer Chatter

October is Computer Learning Month. One of the first computers was built in the early 1940s by Howard Aiken. It was called the Mark I and used 530 miles of wire.

Find each computer word from the Word Bank in the puzzle. The words will go forward, backward, up, down, and diagonally. Then, starting with the first uncircled letter, write every other uncircled letter on the blanks below to answer the riddle.

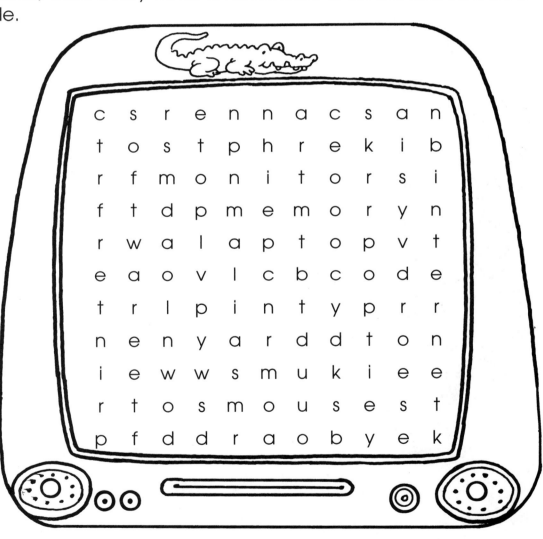

Word Bank

byte
compact disk
download
Internet
keyboard
laptop
memory
monitor
mouse
printer
scanner
software
virus

Where do computers sit at school?

___ ___ ___ ___ ___ ___ ___ ___ ___ ___

___ ___ ___ ___ ___ ___ !

Halloween

Name _____

An Incredible Feast

Halloween has been celebrated in many countries for centuries. For many years, it included a feast for those who led good lives.

Follow each word from the Word Bank through the maze to get the bats to the candy. The words will go across, up, and down.

Word Bank		
costumes	eerie	gloomy
haunted	jack-o-lantern	monster
mummy	October	pumpkin
skeleton	spider	

Name _____

Bony Banter

Write the Halloween word for each definition. The bolded boxes will answer the riddle below.

1. parts of a skeleton

2. a disguise

3. causing a feeling of fear; rhymes with sleepy

4. a very dark color

5. what you get at Halloween

6. the sound an owl makes

7. a small furry flying animal

8. Earth's satellite

Why did the skeleton sit outside?

To get a _____!

23

Name _____

Today's Forecast

On November 1, 1870, the United States Weather Bureau made its first weather observations. Today, weather satellites orbit Earth continuously to gather information about the weather.

Use the Word Bank to write the weather word for each definition on pages 24 and 25. Then, use the number code to fill in the boxes below the definitions to discover three more weather words.

Word Bank			
barometer	blizzard	flood	foggy
forecast	humidity	hurricane	lightning
measure	satellite	sleet	spring
sprinkle	thunder	tornado	weather

1. freezing rain __ __ __ __ __
                   8   4 3

2. full of low clouds __ __ __ __ __
                     10   11

3. to cover with water __ __ __ __ __
                   7 5

4. a funnel of wind __ __ __ __ __ __ __
                  6   9

5. to find the amount __ __ __ __ __ __ __
        1 2

1	2	3	4	5	6	7	8	9	10	11

First Weather Observations

Name _____

6. the condition of the air ___ ___ ___ ___ ___ ___ ___ ___
                                          8   2

7. to predict the weather ___ ___ ___ ___ ___ ___ ___ ___
                                12   4   9

8. a loud, rumbling sound ___ ___ ___ ___ ___ ___ ___
                                  13   3

9. the season before summer ___ ___ ___ ___ ___ ___
                                6   5

10. to rain gently ___ ___ ___ ___ ___ ___ ___
                            1   7

11. a flash of light caused by ___ ___ ___ ___ ___ ___ ___ ___ ___
    electricity moving between clouds   10   11

1	2	3	4	5	6	7	8	9	10	11	12	13

12. a spacecraft used to ___ ___ ___ ___ ___ ___ ___ ___ ___
    forecast the weather   8   3

13. a storm with strong winds ___ ___ ___ ___ ___ ___ ___ ___ ___
                          2   11   10

14. a heavy snowstorm ___ ___ ___ ___ ___ ___ ___ ___
                                  4

15. water vapor in the air ___ ___ ___ ___ ___ ___ ___ ___
                       7   9

16. an instrument used to ___ ___ ___ ___ ___ ___ ___ ___
    measure the pressure of   6   5   1
    the atmosphere

1	2	3	4	5	6	7	8	9	10	11

Take a Ride

There are many ways we get from one place to another. On November 5, 1895, George Seldon of Rochester, New York, received the first patent for this very important type of transportation.

To find out what the patent was for, complete the crossword puzzle. Then, unscramble the shaded letters on the blanks.

_____ _____ _____ _____ _____ _____ _____ _____

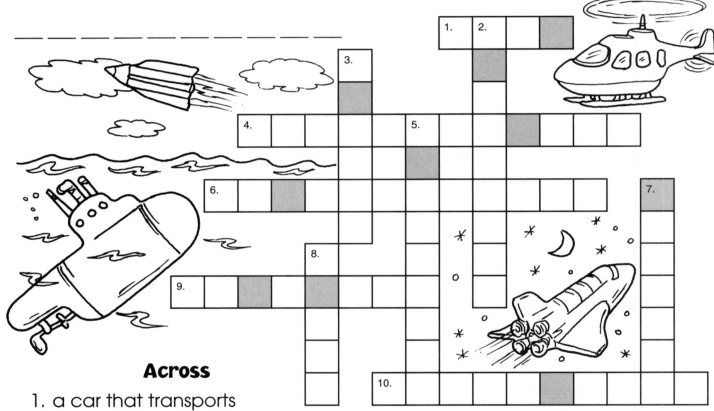

Across

1. a car that transports passengers to where they want to go

4. a spacecraft that returns to land on Earth

6. in-line skates

9. a small room that can be raised or lowered.

10. an aircraft with blades above it

Down

2. transports sick people

3. a spacecraft driven through the air by a stream of hot gasses

5. a ship that travels under water

7. a vehicle with two wheels

8. a large, luxury boat

Name _____

A Slam Dunk

James Naismith, the inventor of basketball, was born on November 6, 1861. *Incredible* and *unbelievable* are two synonyms which describe many basketball players.

One of these incredible basketball players is Michael Jordan. Use the letters from his name and the synonym clues to complete the puzzle. Then, use the number code to complete part of a quote by this unbelievable athlete.

M

I __ __   thing
   18 15

C __ __ __   hat
   8 3 10

H __ __ __   search
        19 5

A __ __ __ __   upstairs
     11 14 1 7

E __ __ __ __ __   flee
         3 10 9

L __ __ __ __ __ __   attorneys
     6   17

J __ __ __ __ __   younger
       4   13 16

O __ __ __ __   possessor
         12

R __ __ __   wealthy
         2

D __ __   mutt
         20

A __   there

N

"I can accept failure...

But ___ ___ ___ ___ ___ '
      1   2 3 4 5

___ ___ ___ ___ ___ ___
 6   7   8   9 10 11

___ ___ ___
12 13 14

___ ___ ___ ___ ___ ___ . "
15 16 17 18 19 20

A Purr-fect Pet

Cat Week begins on the first Sunday in November. Wildcats were first tamed about 5,000 years ago. Some people had pet cats 4,000 years ago.

To find out who these people were, write a word for each definition. Each word has the letters *C*, *A*, and *T* in it. The letter *C* has been given for each word as a clue. The bolded boxes will tell you the answer.

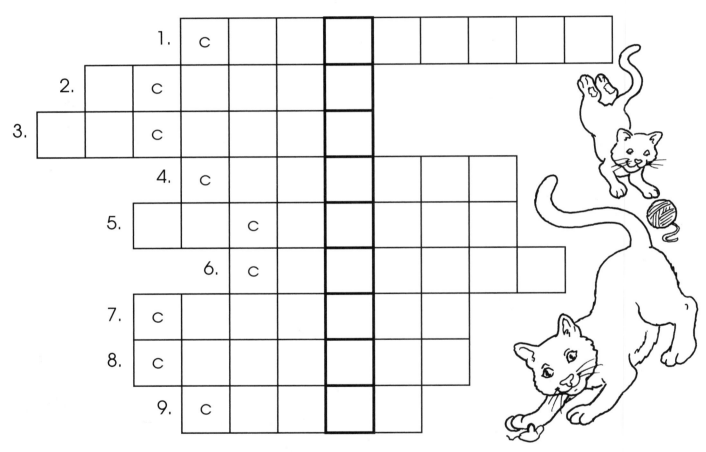

1. to honor a special event

2. pretending

3. a building where things are made

4. a section of a book

5. a period of rest from school

6. the weather conditions in a place

7. a covering for a window

8. a piece of furniture with shelves and doors

9. the land next to the sea

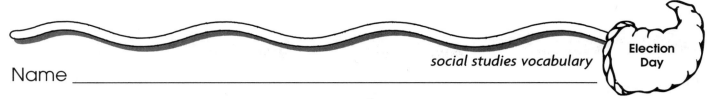

And the Winner Is...

Election Day is held the first Tuesday after the first Monday in November. National elections throughout the United States are held on this day.

Find a path for the ballot to reach the ballot box. Follow the letters of the words about elections from the Word Bank forward, backward, up, down, and diagonally.

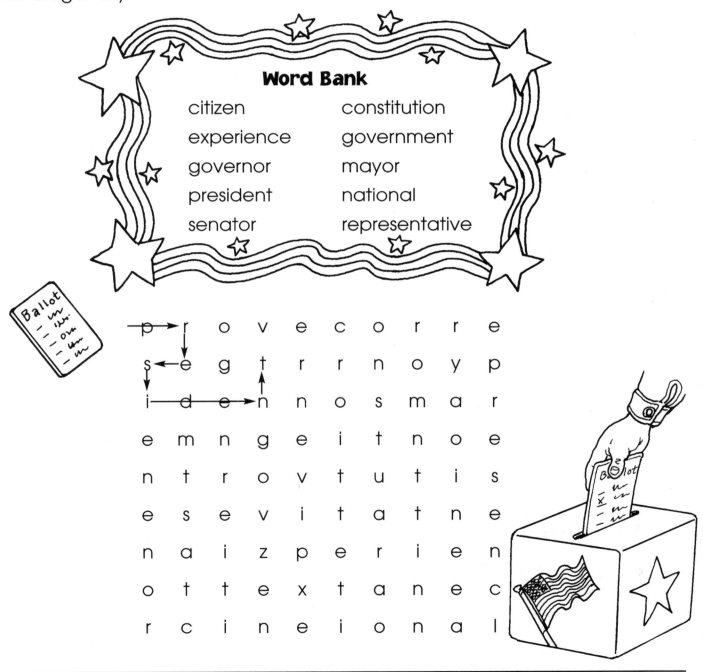

Word Bank

citizen	constitution
experience	government
governor	mayor
president	national
senator	representative

Name _____

A Cold Trip South

Captain Nathanial Palmer is believed to have discovered Antarctica on November 18, 1820. The South Pole is located there. Another American made many expeditions in the early 1900s to this unpopulated continent.

To find out his name, unscramble the following words with the *ar* sound. Use the sentences as clues. Then, write the shaded letters in order on the blanks below.

1. A R T P　　☐☐▨☐　　I like that _____ of the story.

2. A R L S I I M　　☐▨☐☐☐☐☐　　Brown and tan are _____ colors.

3. A R Y C R　　▨☐☐☐☐　　I will _____ the flag.

4. A R V T E S H　　▨☐☐☐☐☐☐☐　　It is time to _____ the corn.

5. A R H E S　　☐☐▨☐☐　　Please _____ the cookies with her.

6. A R F S C　　☐☐☐▨☐　　I wore a _____ because it was cold.

7. A R G N E D　　☐☐☐▨☐☐　　The flowers in the _____ are blooming.

8. A R O R H B　　☐☐☐▨☐☐　　The boat sailed away from the _____.

9. A R Y R M　　☐☐☐☐▨　　My aunt is going to _____ her boyfriend.

10. A R G E A G　　☐☐▨☐☐☐　　My dad put the car in the _____.

11. A R C D S E　　☐☐☐☐☐▨　　The loud noise _____ me.

___ ___ ___ ___ ___ ___ 　 ___ ___ ___ ___ ___

Name _____

A Memorable Speech

On November 19, 1863, President Abraham Lincoln delivered the *Gettysburg Address*. This famous Civil War speech began "Four score and seven years ago . . ."

To find out in which state this speech was delivered, complete the puzzle. Finish each double consonant word. Use the definitions as clues. Then, unscramble the boxed letters on the blanks below.

___ ___ pp___ ☐   1. to provide something needed

___ ☐ ___ pp___ ___   2. a spice often used with salt

☐ ___ ___ pp___   3. very messy

___ ___ ☐ pp___ ___   4. a light shoe easy to put on the foot

___ ☐ l l ___ ___   5. a measurement unit for liquids

☐ ___ l l ___ ___   6. low land between hills or mountains

___ ___ l l ☐ ___ ___   7. a small town

___ ___ l l ☐ ___   8. a school after high school

___ ___ t t ☐   9. a fight during a war

___ ___ t t ___ ☐   10. a type of cloth

___ ___ t t ___ ☐   11. used to fasten a shirt

___ ___ t t ☐   12. spoiled

___ ___ ___ ___ ___ ___ ___ ___ ___ ___ ___

Name _____

Native American Tribes

When the pilgrims arrived, there were many different Native American tribes living in North America. Each tribe's way of life was dependent on the area of the country in which the tribe lived.

Circle the names of the Native American tribes listed below. The names will go forward, backward, up, down, and diagonally.

Anasazi   Apache   Cherokee
Cheyenne   Choctaw   Iroquois
Navajo   Seminole   Seneca
Shawnee   Shoshoni
Sioux   Ute

```
C H E Y U S H A I A N
H O N A T A W P N P A
O N N I R O Q U O I S
C I E A C H E R H U O
E A Y Q V U M J S A W
N C E X W A T C O H C
A E H U E E J E H U H
P N C O T A W O S T E
A E A I R O Q J I S R
C S Q S E E V A J O O
H E S H A W N E E I K
E Y T A W Z A Z I S E
I R O S E M I N O L E
```

Name _____

A Day to Feast

Thanksgiving is celebrated on the fourth Thursday in November. It is the oldest American holiday.

Thanksgiving is a compound word. Use the picture clues to write more compound words on the lines. Then, use the number code to answer the Thanksgiving riddle below.

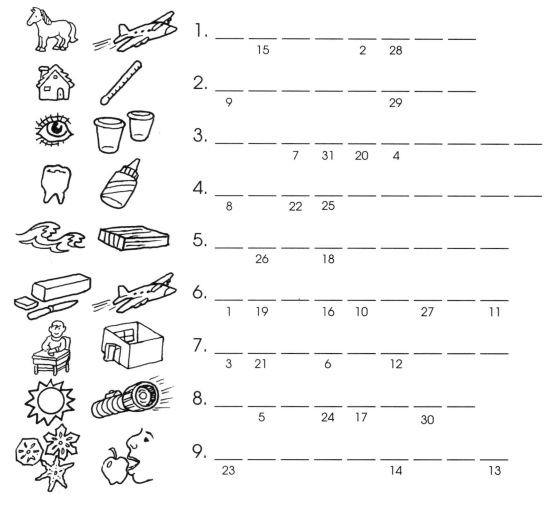

1. ___ ___ ___ ___ ___ ___ ___
   15   2 28

2. ___ ___ ___ ___ ___ ___
 9   29

3. ___ ___ ___ ___ ___ ___ ___ ___ ___ ___
    7 31 20 4

4. ___ ___ ___ ___ ___ ___ ___
 8   22 25

5. ___ ___ ___ ___ ___
  26   18

6. ___ ___ ___ ___ ___ ___ ___ ___ ___
 1 19   16 10   27   11

7. ___ ___ ___ ___ ___ ___ ___
 3 21   6   12

8. ___ ___ ___ ___ ___ ___
   5   24 17 30

9. ___ ___ ___ ___ ___ ___
 23   14   13

Why is a couch like a turkey?

___ ___ ___ ___ ___ ___ ___   ___ ___ ___ ___   ___ ___ ___ ___ ___
1 2 3 4 5 6 7   8 9 10 11 12 13 14 15 16 17

___ ___ ___ ___   ___ ___   ___ ___ ___ ___ ___ ___ ___ ___ !
18 19 20 21 22 23 24 25 26 27 28 29 30 31

Festival of Lights

Hanukkah is a Jewish holiday also known as the Festival of Lights. It is celebrated for eight days. A candle is lit each night during this celebration.

Use the sentence and synonym clues below to fill in each set of boxes. Then, write each letter from the bolded boxes in order in the last set of boxes to learn the name of a special candleholder.

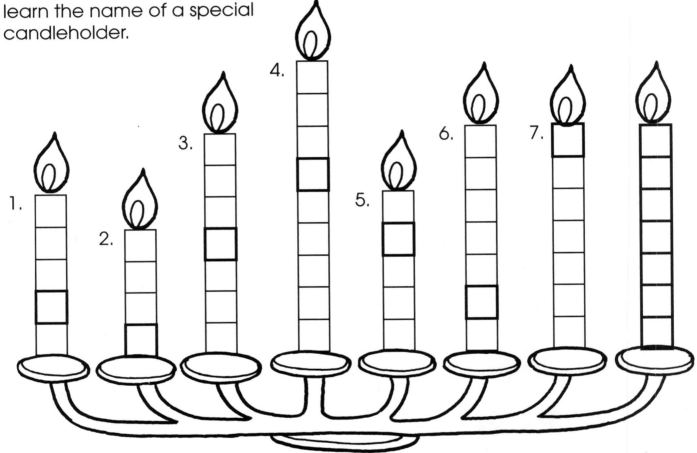

1. The _____ of the candle is orange. (fire)

2. The family celebrates in their _____. (habitat)

3. In the _____, they light the candle. (night)

4. Hanukkah is an _____ Jewish holiday. (significant)

5. Ian is _____ of his family. (pleased)

6. Each night the family opens a _____ gift. (outstanding)

7. Rachel was excited for the _____ season. (vacation)

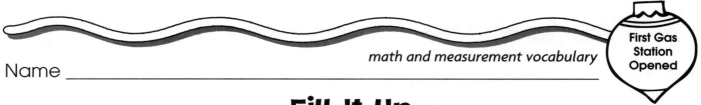

Name _____

Fill It Up

On December 1, 1913, the first gas station was opened in Pittsburgh, Pennsylvania.

To find out how much gas was sold the first day, complete the puzzle using the math and measurement clues. Then, read the first letter of each word to learn the amount.

1. 10 times 100

2. the distance from top to bottom

3. the 12 parts of a foot

4. a 12-inch straight edge used to measure objects

5. between second and fourth

6. a measurement equal to three feet

7. a metric unit of weight less than an ounce

8. the adding of numbers

9. the distance from one end to the other

10. a metric unit similar to a quart

11. a small unit of weight

12. 10 less than 100

13. the 60 parts of a minute

Name _____

Deep Freeze

Clarence Birdseye was the founder of the frozen-foods industry. He was born on December 9, 1886, in Brooklyn, New York.

Complete each analogy. The shaded boxes will spell three frozen- food products.

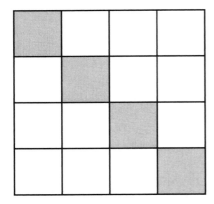

1. Shovel is to digging as _____ is to fishing.

2. North is to south as east is to _____.

3. Long is to short as _____ is to messy.

4. Fingers are to hand as _____ are to foot.

5. Warm is to hot as cool is to _____.

6. Worker is to _____ as player is to coach.

7. Boats are to river as _____ are to road.

8. High is to low as up is to _____.

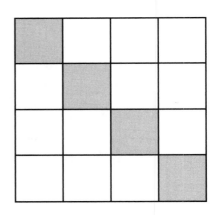

9. Real is to fantasy as _____ is to opinion.

10. County is to state as suburb is to _____.

11. Satisfied is to win as disappointed is to _____.

12. Cup is to drink as _____ is to eat.

Name _____

A Long Journey

On December 13, 1577, Sir Francis Drake set sail from Plymouth, England. It took him three years to sail around the world.

Finish each sentence in the center of the puzzle with a three-syllable word from the Word Bank. Write each word in the puzzle around the world. Be careful; not all the words from the Word Bank will be used. The shaded letters will spell the name of Sir Francis Drake's ship.

Word Bank

adventure	Atlantic	century	continue
dangerous	decision	discover	estimate
history	messenger	Pacific	pioneer

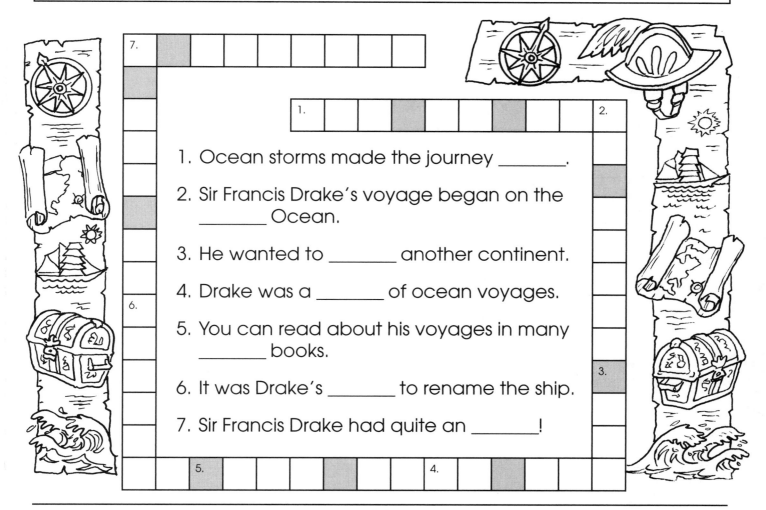

1. Ocean storms made the journey _____.

2. Sir Francis Drake's voyage began on the _____ Ocean.

3. He wanted to _____ another continent.

4. Drake was a _____ of ocean voyages.

5. You can read about his voyages in many _____ books.

6. It was Drake's _____ to rename the ship.

7. Sir Francis Drake had quite an _____!

World's First Airplane Flight

Name _____

Flying High

On December 17, 1903, Orville and Wilbur Wright completed the first airplane flight near Kitty Hawk, North Carolina.

To find out how long the first flight lasted, complete the puzzle. In each set of boxes, write the homophone for the missing word in each sentence. The bolded boxes will tell how long this flight was.

1. Beth climbed every _____ to the top of the building.

2. His _____ has changed to 70 pounds.

3. The bridge was made of _____ .

4. The man was so tall that he bumped his head on the _____ .

5. John is a _____ good skater.

6. Mom will _____ the cheese for the pizza.

7. I need to _____ the seeds before it rains.

8. We sailed across the _____ .

9. Your clean _____ are in the laundry basket.

10. Rayna was _____ because there was nothing to do.

11. The _____ rode his horse to the castle.

12. We need a _____ to clean your messy room.

13. My feet were _____ from walking all day.

Name _____

Read the Clue

On December 21, 1913, the first crossword puzzle appeared in the *New York World* newspaper. This type of word puzzle is still popular today.

Complete the crossword puzzle with a word containing a silent letter.

Across

1. behaving badly

4. powerful

6. to be very hungry

7. to cover a package

8. a long reptile with no legs

9. a legend

10. from another country

Down

1. a sound

2. what a clock measures

3. good-looking

5. awful, terrible

Name _____

Cold and Hot

The shortest day of each year in the northern hemisphere occurs on December 21 or 22. This date marks the beginning of winter. At this same time, the southern hemisphere is having the opposite season (summer).

Write the antonym for each clue. Then, unscramble the circled letters on the lines below to spell a winter word.

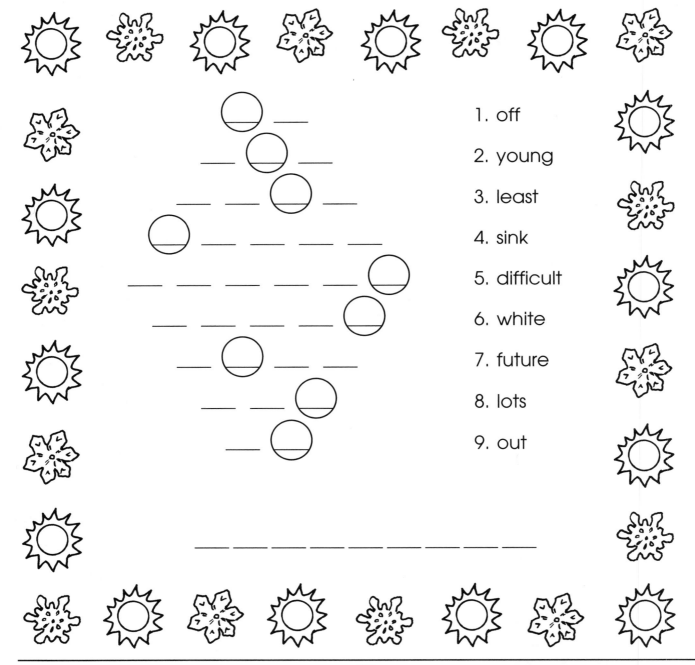

1. off

2. young

3. least

4. sink

5. difficult

6. white

7. future

8. lots

9. out

Name _____

A Jolly Season

Christmas is celebrated all over the world on December 25. There are many customs and traditions associated with this Christian holiday.

One custom is to decorate an evergreen tree. Use each letter in the tree lights and each one-word clue to write 10 Christmas words.

1. __ __ __ __ __ __ __ __ __
   (decoration)

2. __ __ __ __ __ __ __ __ __
   (antlers)

3. __ __ __ __ __ __ __
   (wrap)

4. __ __ __ __ __ __ __ __
   (singing)

5. __ __ __ __ __ __ __
   (worship)

6. __ __ __ __ __ __ __ __ __ __ __
   (mantel)

7. __ __ __ __ __ __ __ __
   (fireplace)

8. __ __ __ __ __ __
   (sled)

9. __ __ __ __ __ __
   (door)

10. __ __ __ __ __
    (calm)

Kwanzaa Celebration

Kwanzaa is a seven-day holiday that lasts from December 26 until January 1. It celebrates African cultures and the lives of African-Americans. The name *Kwanzaa* comes from Swahili words which mean "first fruits."

Circle the Kwanzaa celebration words in the puzzle. The words will go forward, backward, up, down, and diagonally. Then, write the remaining letters in order on the blanks below to spell the Swahili words from which the name *Kwanzaa* comes.

ancestors
art
black
candles
culture
dance
faith
family
feast
fun
gifts
green
harvest
honor
music
purpose
tradition
unity
red

```
a  e  r  u  t  l  u  c  y  g  h
t  n  m  h  o  n  o  r  l  r  a
r  k  c  a  l  b  a  t  i  e  r
a  u  a  e  n  f  u  n  m  e  v
d  d  n  s  s  y  e  a  a  n  e
i  s  d  o  h  t  i  a  f  a  s
t  t  l  p  y  i  o  a  s  r  t
i  f  e  r  k  n  w  r  a  t  n
o  i  s  u  e  u  m  u  s  i  c
n  g  z  p  a  d  a  n  c  e  a
```

___ ___ ___ ___ ___ ___ ___   ___ ___ ___ ___ ___ ___

Name _____

A Sweet-Smelling Parade

Everyone loves a parade! The Tournament of Roses Parade is held on New Year's Day in Pasadena, California. The founders of this parade wanted to celebrate California's warm weather. The opposite kind of weather, cold and snowy, was happening in much of the rest of the country.

Write the antonym of each clue in the puzzle. The last letter of each word will be the first letter of the next word. Then, unscramble the letters from the shaded boxes to find out what is used to make the floats in this parade. Write the answer on the blanks below.

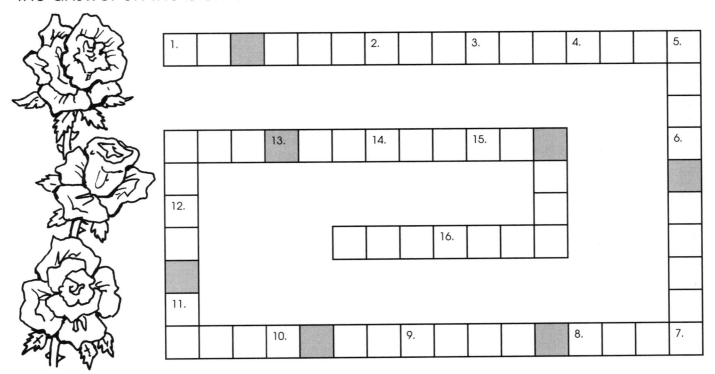

1. solution	2. freeze	3. wild	4. enter
5. fat	6. farthest	7. false	8. capture
9. late	10. old	11. frown	12. wide
13. strong	14. mean	15. same	16. huge

___ ___ ___ ___ ___ ___ ___

Name _____

A Super System

Louis Braille was born on January 4, 1809, near Paris, France. He developed a system of reading called Braille.

To learn more about this remarkable man and this reading system, use the system to complete the passage.

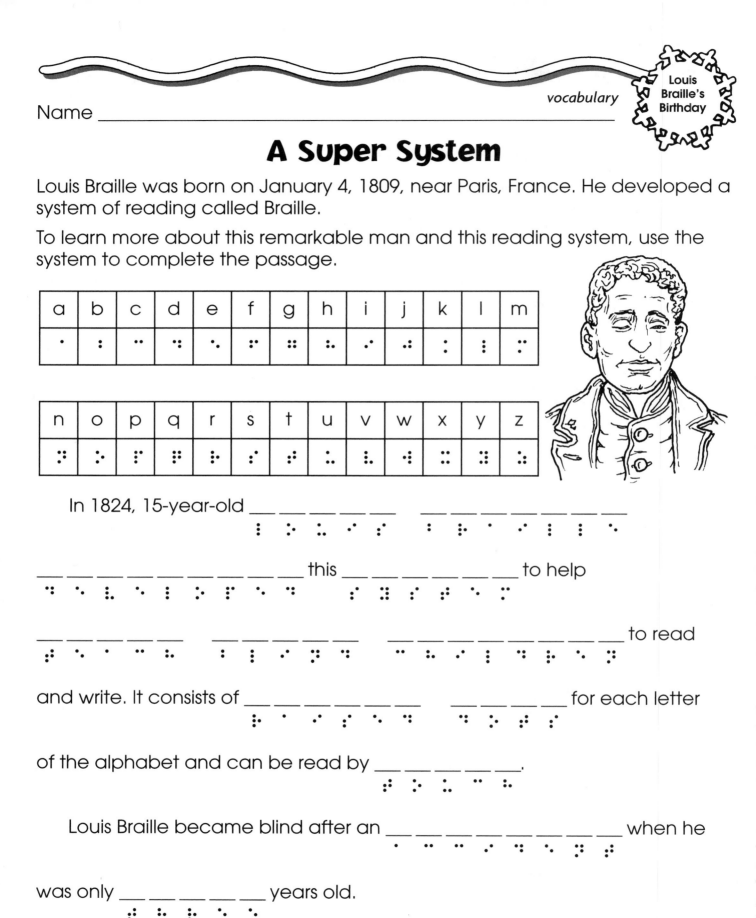

In 1824, 15-year-old ___ ___ ___ ___ ___   ___ ___ ___ ___ ___ ___ ___

___ ___ ___ ___ ___ ___ ___ ___ ___ this ___ ___ ___ ___ ___ to help

___ ___ ___ ___ ___   ___ ___ ___ ___   ___ ___ ___ ___ ___ ___ ___ to read

and write. It consists of ___ ___ ___ ___ ___ ___   ___ ___ ___ ___ for each letter

of the alphabet and can be read by ___ ___ ___ ___ ___.

Louis Braille became blind after an ___ ___ ___ ___ ___ ___ ___ ___ ___ when he

was only ___ ___ ___ ___ ___ years old.

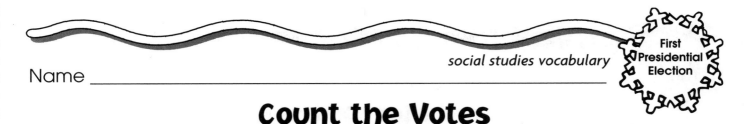

Name _____

First Presidential Election

Count the Votes

On January 7, 1789, the first presidential election was held in the United States. George Washington was elected. The person who finished second became the vice president.

To find out his name, unscramble the names of the states which participated in the first election. Then, write the circled letters in order to spell the name of the vice president.

1. wne seejyr   __ __ __ Ⓞ __ __ __ __

2. stasmetshcuas   __ __ __ __ __ __ Ⓞ __ __ __ __ __ __

3. cuttinencoc   __ __ Ⓞ __ __ __ __ __ __ __

4. raivinig   __ __ __ __ __ __ __ __

5. senplnavyain   __ __ __ __ __ __ __ Ⓞ __ __ __

6. nwe phraemhis   __ __ __ __ Ⓞ __ __ __ __ __ __

7. wlearead   Ⓞ __ __ __ __ __ __ __

8. raigoeg   __ __ Ⓞ __ __ __ __

9. dlarmyan   Ⓞ __ __ __ __ __ __ __

10. thuos raonialc   Ⓞ __ __ __ __ __ __ __ __ __ __ __ __

Vice President __ __ __ __ __ __ __ __ __ __

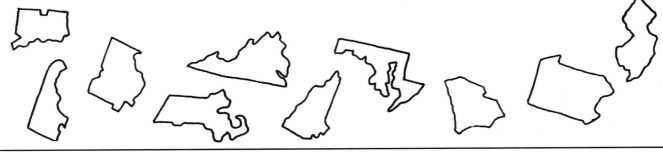

Name _____

An Historic Flight

On January 11, 1935, Amelia Earhart became the first woman to fly solo across the Pacific Ocean, from Hawaii to California.

To find out where she began this 18-hour flight, complete the puzzle. Write the word in the puzzle from the Word Bank that completes each sentence about Amelia Earhart. Then, write the letters from the shaded boxes in order on the blanks below to learn the city where this historic flight began.

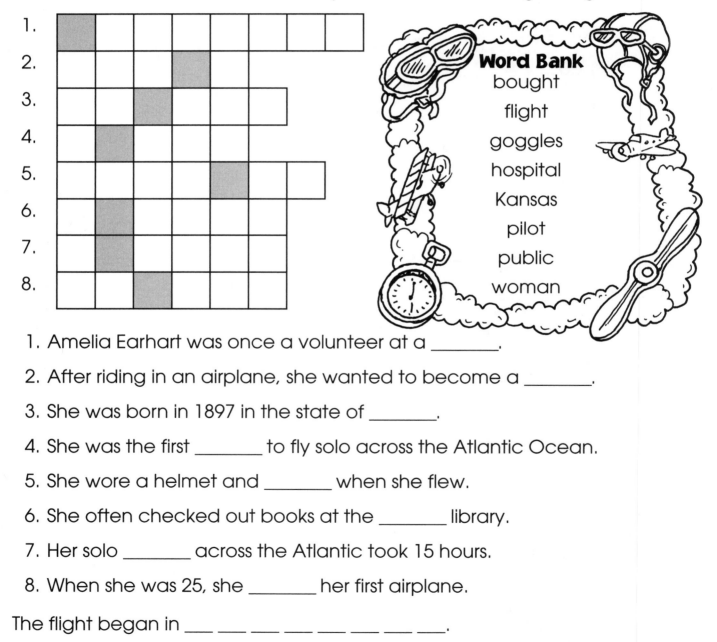

Word Bank

bought

flight

goggles

hospital

Kansas

pilot

public

woman

1. Amelia Earhart was once a volunteer at a _____.

2. After riding in an airplane, she wanted to become a _____.

3. She was born in 1897 in the state of _____.

4. She was the first _____ to fly solo across the Atlantic Ocean.

5. She wore a helmet and _____ when she flew.

6. She often checked out books at the _____ library.

7. Her solo _____ across the Atlantic took 15 hours.

8. When she was 25, she _____ her first airplane.

The flight began in ___ ___ ___ ___ ___ ___ ___ ___.

 Word Games: Grades 3–4

Name _____

The Freedom Doctor

Martin Luther King, Jr. was born on January 15, 1929. Dr. King's birthday became a national holiday in 1983 and is celebrated on the third Monday in January.

Write the word from the Word Bank in the puzzle for each definition. Not all the words will be used. Then, write the letters from the bolded boxes in order on the blanks below to learn the name of the famous speech given by Dr. King.

Word Bank

author
boycott
civil rights
discrimination
eloquent
equality
justice
intelligent
leader
minister
movement
nonviolent
protesters
segregation

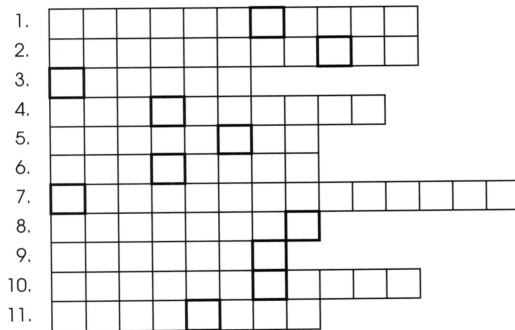

1. very smart and wise

2. the qualities of personal liberties

3. a person who writes a book

4. not forceful

5. using words well

6. the condition of being equal

7. an unfair difference in treatment

8. a person who conducts a church service

9. fair treatment

10. the practice of setting one racial group apart from another

11. the actions of a group to reach some goal

The name of the speech is "___ __ __ __ __ __ __ __ __ __ __ __ __."

Name _____

Doctor Blackwell

The first woman in the United States to receive a medical degree was Elizabeth Blackwell. On January 23, 1849, in Geneva, New York, Elizabeth became Dr. Blackwell.

Write each medical word in the puzzle. Start with the word with the most letters.

Word Bank

anatomy

artery

disease

emergency

examination

immunization

internist

medicine

physician

specialist

stethoscope

surgeon

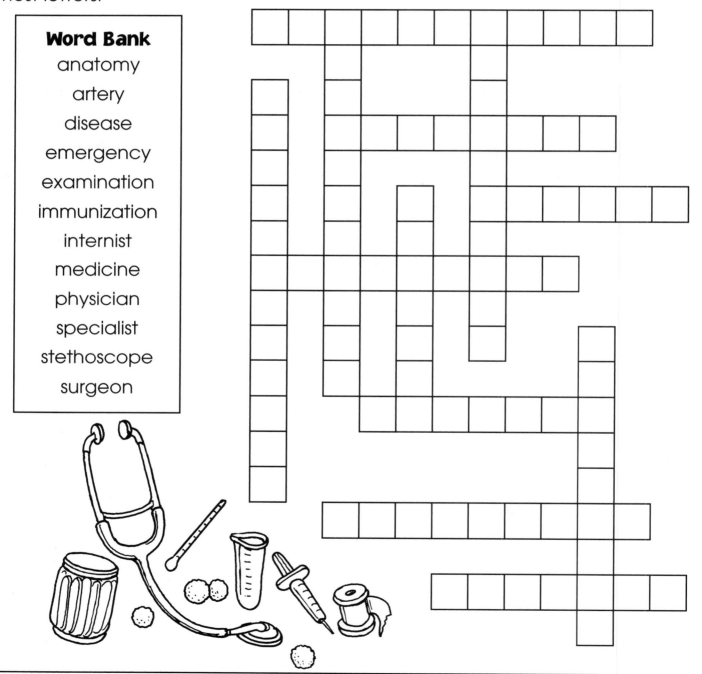

Gold Discovered in California

Name _____

Strike It Rich

James Marshall discovered gold in California on January 24, 1848. For the next two years, thousands rushed to California in search of gold. They were nicknamed "forty-niners."

Use the clues to complete the puzzles with the words forty and niners.

1. before second

2. gives a car power

3. being born

4. not clean

5. to rush

6. not wide

7. it shows a reflection

8. one who dances

9. a part of speech

10. to tell about something

11. large animals with manes

National
Kazoo
Day

Name That Tune

National Kazoo Day is celebrated in late January. By humming into this instrument, you can play any song you want.

Complete the puzzle using the clues to the right. Each word will contain *oo* in it.

___ ___ ___   1. cow sound

___ ___ ___ ___   2. sheep hair

___ ___ ___ ___ ___   3. flower parts

___ ___ ___ ___ ___ ___   4. short sleep

___ ___ ___ ___ ___ ___ ___   5. hair wash

___ ___ ___ ___ ___ ___ ___   6. sidewalk vehicle

___ ___ ___ ___ ___ ___   7. not rough

___ ___ ___ ___ ___   8. chewing tool

___ ___ ___ ___   9. part of tree used to build things

___ ___ ___   10. place for animals

Name _____

Double Play

On January 29, 1936, the Baseball Hall of Fame was established. It opened in Cooperstown, New York, in 1939. Walter Johnson, Christy Mathewson, and Honus Wagner were three of the first five members.

To find out the names of the other two players, find a single word for each group that makes three compound words. Then, use the number code to write the players' names on the lines on page 52.

1. __ __ __ __ __ fall
       13

   __ __ __ __ __ __ color

   __ __ __ __ __ __ melon

2. __ __ __ field
      12

   __ __ __ fit

   __ __ __ side

3. __ __ __ __ coat
   11

   __ __ __ __ bow

   __ __ __ __ fall

4. __ __ __ plane
   8

   __ __ __ mail

   __ __ __ tight

5. __ __ __ __ walk
      10

   __ __ __ __ line

   __ __ __ __ ways

6. __ __ __ __ __ print
       1

   __ __ __ __ __ step

   __ __ __ __ __ ball

7. straw __ __ __ __ __
      5   2

   blue __ __ __ __ __

   goose __ __ __ __ __
       7

8. sail __ __ __ __
      6

   house __ __ __ __

   motor __ __ __ __
        9

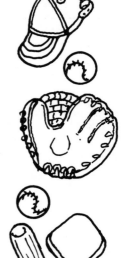

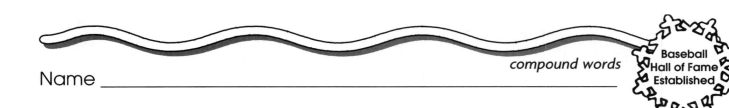

Baseball
Hall of Fame
Established

9. __ __ __ __ one
   $\overset{}{\underset{4}{}}$

   __ __ __ __ time

   __ __ __ __ day

10. __ __ __ shine

    __ __ __ flower

    __ __ __ glasses

11. __ __ __ __ cuff
    $\overset{}{\underset{14}{}}$

    __ __ __ __ writing

    __ __ __ __ made

12. __ __ __ __ fire
    $\overset{}{\underset{3}{}}$

    __ __ __ __ ground

    __ __ __ __ site

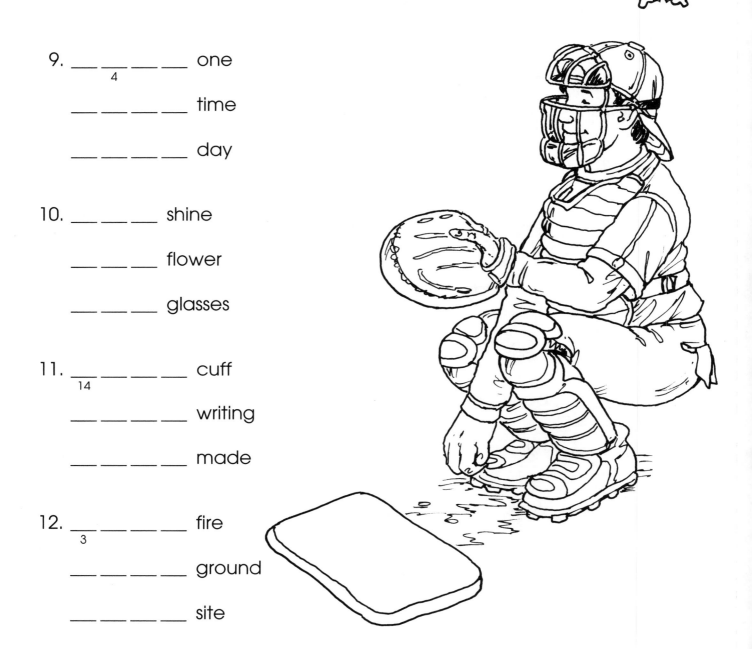

__ __ __   __ __ __ __   and   __ __ __ __   __ __ __ __
 1   2   3 4 5 6   7 8 9 10   11 12 13 14

Incredible Americans

February is African-American History Month. In 1926, Carter G. Woodson started this month-long tribute as a time to learn about many important African-Americans.

Follow each name of an important African-American from the Name Bank through the maze. The names will go forward, backward, up, and down.

Name Bank

Maya Angelou

Jackie Joyner-Kersee

Jesse Owens

Colin Powell

Clarence Thomas

Louis Armstrong

Thurgood Marshall

Rosa Parks

Jackie Robinson

Harriet Tubman

George Washington Carver

Sidney Poitier

Wilma Rudolph

Carter G. Woodson

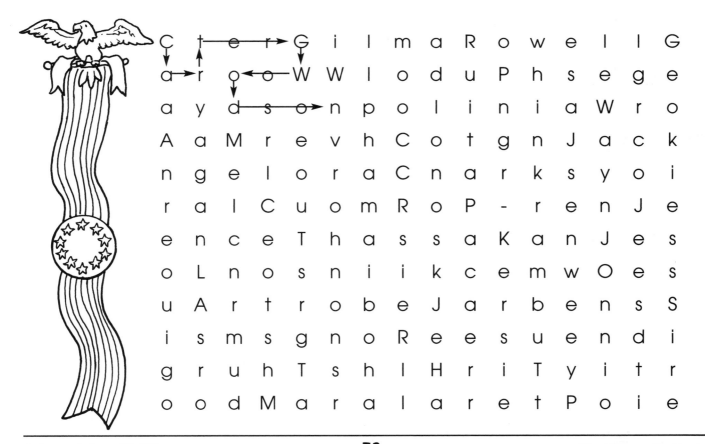

```
C  t  e     G  i  l  m  a  R  o  w  e  l  l  G
a  r  o  W  W  l  o  d  u  P  h  s  e  g  e
a  y  d  s  o  n  p  o  l  i  n  i  a  W  r  o
A  a  M  r  e  v  h  C  o  t  g  n  J  a  c  k
n  g  e  l  o  r  a  C  n  a  r  k  s  y  o  i
r  a  l  C  u  o  m  R  o  P  -  r  e  n  J  e
e  n  c  e  T  h  a  s  s  a  K  a  n  J  e  s
o  L  n  o  s  n  i  i  k  c  e  m  w  O  e  s
u  A  r  t  r  o  b  e  J  a  r  b  e  n  s  S
i  s  m  s  g  n  o  R  e  e  s  u  e  n  d  i
g  r  u  h  T  s  h  l  H  r  i  T  y  i  t  r
o  o  d  M  a  r  a  l  a  r  e  t  P  o  i  e
```

Name _____

Brush and Floss

National Children's Dental Health Week begins the first Sunday in February.

Find each word about dental health from the Word Bank in the puzzle. The words will go up, down, forward, backward, and diagonally. Then, to learn a fact about teeth, write the letters remaining in order on the blanks below.

Word Bank			
bicuspids	bite	calcium	canines
cavity	dentin	dentist	enamel
fluoride	gum	incisors	molars
plaque	pulp	orthodontist	root
tartar	toothbrush		

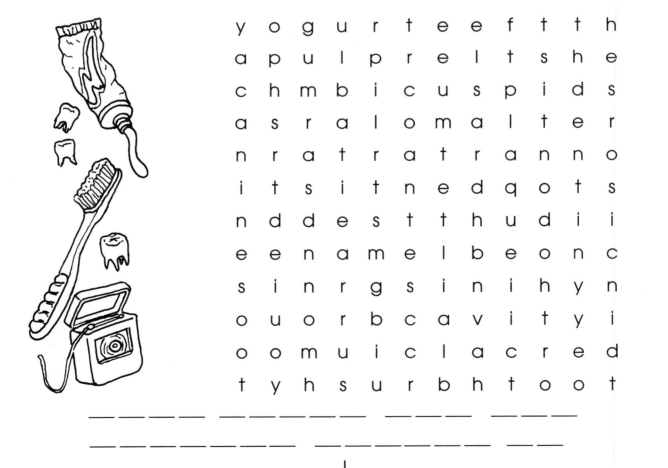

```
y  o  g  u  r  t  e  e  f  t  t  h
a  p  u  l  p  r  e  l  t  s  h  e
c  h  m  b  i  c  u  s  p  i  d  s
a  s  r  a  l  o  m  a  l  t  e  r
n  r  a  t  r  a  t  r  a  n  n  o
i  t  s  i  t  n  e  d  q  o  t  s
n  d  d  e  s  t  t  h  u  d  i  i
e  e  n  a  m  e  l  b  e  o  n  c
s  i  n  r  g  s  i  n  i  h  y  n
o  u  o  r  b  c  a  v  i  t  y  i
o  o  m  u  i  c  l  a  c  r  e  d
t  y  h  s  u  r  b  h  t  o  o  t
```

_____ _____ _____ _____ _____ _____ _____

_____ _____ _____ _____ _____ _____

_____ _____ _____!

Name _____

Is Spring Here?

Groundhog Day is celebrated on February 2. The pilgrims brought this tradition to America from England.

Write a word for each definition. Then, use the number code to discover two words about this special day. To learn about this tradition, fill in the missing words in the passage below with words from the activity.

1. the second month of the year

___ ___ ___ ___ ___ ___ ___ ___
  18 12 14

2. a dark area made by blocked light

___ ___ ___ ___ ___ ___ ___
               1

3. an opening

___ ___ ___ ___
10

4. a custom that is passed along

___ ___ ___ ___ ___ ___ ___ ___ ___
                17   3 15

5. opposite of front

___ ___ ___ ___
  16 8 9

6. giving light

___ ___ ___ ___ ___ ___ ___
  6

7. the season after winter

___ ___ ___ ___ ___ ___
        11

8. a day without sun

___ ___ ___ ___ ___ ___
5   2 7 4

9. a place where wild animals sleep

___ ___ ___
13

1	2	3	4	5	6	7	8	9

10	11	12	13	14	15	16	17	18

The groundhog, or _____, is a large rodent. The American _____ says that on the morning of _____ 2, the groundhog comes out of its _____ and looks around. If the sun is _____ and the groundhog sees its _____, it will be scared _____ into its _____ and will _____ for six more weeks. If the day is _____, the groundhog will stay out, and _____ will arrive soon.

Name _____

Earn Some Cash

The first paper money in America was issued on February 3, 1690, in Massachusetts. It was used to pay soldiers.

Use each letter group from the Letter Bank to make a five-letter word on each piece of paper money. Use each letter group only once.

Letter Bank				
tr	ave	~~ey~~	oup	cr
ten	pow	sc	er	ize
~~mon~~	gr	~~per~~	ade	~~pa~~
ore	pr	owd	th	br

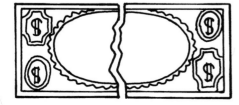

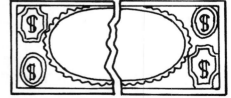

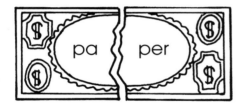

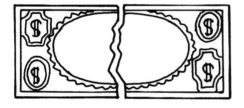

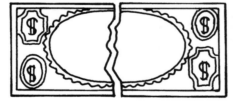

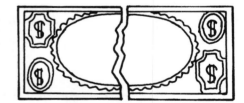

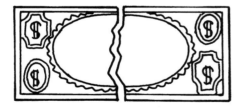

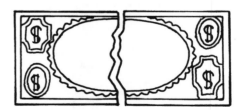

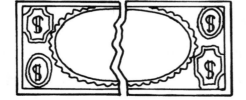

Name _____

Time for School

The first public school in America was started on February 13, 1635, in Boston, Massachusetts. It was called the Boston Latin School.

Starting at the bottom of each puzzle, fill in the boxes with words about school from the Word Bank. The last letter of each word is the first letter of the next word.

Word Bank

desk

help

kindergarten

know

listen

math

paper

read

recess

school

teacher

test

think

write

Around and Around

George Washington Gale Ferris was born on February 14, 1859, in Galesburg, Illinois. He invented the Ferris wheel to celebrate the 400th anniversary of Christopher Columbus's discovery of the New World.

Write a word in each seat of the Ferris wheel using the words from the Word Bank and the definitions. Not all of the words will be used.

Word Bank

beef
bleed
breeze
creek
freeze
greed
keep
peek
seek
sleep
sleeve
speed
steel
weed

1. quick motion

2. meat from a cow

3. to loose blood

4. a small stream

5. to rest

6. to save

7. to look quickly

8. to try to find

9. hard, strong metal

10. to harden because of the cold

11. a plant that is not wanted

Name _____

A Sweet Smell

Valentine's Day is celebrated on February 14. The rose has been called the flower of romance and is often sent to another person on this day as a token of love.

Use the definitions to unscramble each word about flowers. Then, write the letter in each shaded box in order to answer the riddle below.

1. m t s e   ☐☐☐☐   the part that supports a flower

2. c h u n b   ☐☐☐☐☐   a group of flowers

3. l u b b   ☐☐☐☐   underground part from which some flowers grow

4. s i y a d   ☐☐☐☐☐   a type of flower with a yellow center

5. a t l e p   ☐☐☐☐☐   colorful part of a flower

6. e r s o   ☐☐☐☐   a flower with a thorny stem

What flower does most everyone have?

___ ___ ___ ___ ___

Name _____

Circling Earth

On February 20, 1962, John Glenn became the first American to orbit the Earth. He circled the Earth three times during this historic flight.

To learn the name of Glenn's spacecraft, complete each analogy. The bolded boxes will spell the name of the spacecraft.

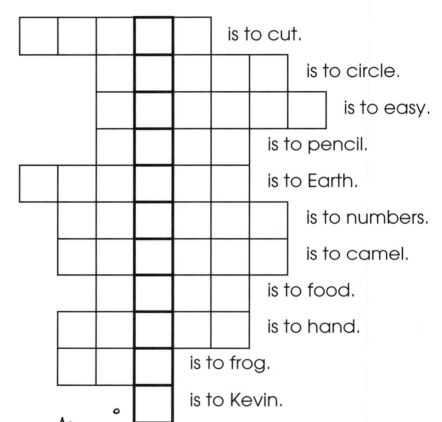

1. Pencil is to write as   is to cut.

2. Split is to divide as   is to circle.

3. Difficult is to hard as   is to easy.

4. Ink is to pen as   is to pencil.

5. Continent is to Asia as   is to Earth.

6. Spelling is to letters as   is to numbers.

7. Ocean is to whale as   is to camel.

8. Sip is to drink as   is to food.

9. Ankle is to foot as   is to hand.

10. Gallop is to horse as   is to frog.

11. 8 is to Kate as   is to Kevin.

Name _____

The Birthday Bash

Presidents' Day is celebrated on the third Monday in February. Both George Washington and Abraham Lincoln were born during this month. Two other presidents were also born during February.

To find out their names, fit each word about George Washington and Abraham Lincoln into the puzzle. Start with the word or words with the most letters. Then, use the number code to write their names below.

George Washington		Abraham Lincoln	
federalist	first	Civil War	debates
general	Mount Vernon	Gettysburg	Kentucky
plantation	surveyor	lawyer	sixteenth
Virginia		stovepipe hat	

_ _ _ _ _ _ _ _ and _ _ _ _ _ _
1 2 3 4 5 6 7 8   9 10 11 12 13 14

Name _____

A Bite of Health

Eating is one of the most important things we do every day. Nutrition is the study of how the food we eat keeps our bodies going. March is National Nutrition Month and a good time to learn more about nutrition.

Find the words about nutrition from the Word Bank in the puzzle. The words will go forward, backward, up, down, and diagonally. Then, write each remaining letter in order on the blanks below to learn an interesting fact about the body.

Word Bank

- calcium
- calorie
- carbohydrates
- energy
- exercise
- fats
- fruit
- iron
- meat
- milk
- minerals
- muscle
- nutrition
- protein
- vegetable
- vitamins
- water

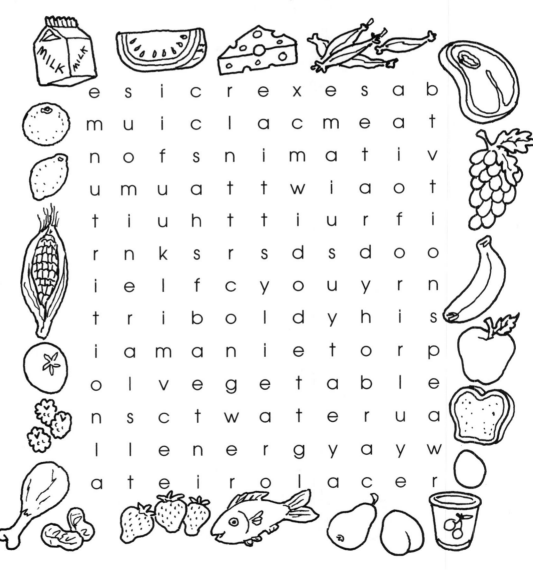

```
e  s  i  c  r  e  x  e  s  a  b
m  u  i  c  l  a  c  m  e  a  t
n  o  f  s  n  i  m  a  t  i  v
u  m  u  a  t  t  w  i  a  o  t
t  i  u  h  t  t  i  u  r  f  i
r  n  k  s  r  s  d  s  d  o  o
i  e  l  f  c  y  o  u  y  r  n
t  r  i  b  o  l  d  y  h  i  s
i  a  m  a  n  i  e  t  o  r  p
o  l  v  e  g  e  t  a  b  l  e
n  s  c  t  w  a  t  e  r  u  a
l  l  e  n  e  r  g  y  a  y  w
a  t  e  i  r  o  l  a  c  e  r
```

_____ _____ _____ _____ _____ _____ - _____ _____ _____ _____   _____ _____ _____

_____ _____ _____   _____ _____ _____ _____ _____ _____   _____ _____ _____ _____!

Name _____

A Winning Woman

Women's History Month is celebrated in March to learn about the lives of important women. The first woman to win the Iditarod Trail Sled Dog Race in Alaska was Libby Riddles in 1985.

The racers in this race are called mushers. To learn more about Libby Riddles and the race, complete each word box using the sentence clues and the letter clues in the puzzle.

1. The race begins in the state of _____.

2. Ms. Riddles _____ books about the race.

3. The race _____ in Anchorage, Alaska.

4. Temperatures can reach 50 degrees _____ zero.

5. The Junior Iditarod is 150 miles for _____ racers.

6. The race begins on the first _____ in March.

7. The race is about 1,200 _____ long.

8. Each musher uses about 2,500 _____ of dog food during the race.

9. Mushers may start the race with 16 _____.

10. The _____ takes the mushers over rugged mountains.

11. This race is the _____ sled dog race in the world.

12. The _____ line is in Nome, Alaska.

Name _____

Sky Jumper

In March of 1912, Albert Berry made the first parachute jump from an airplane. The following year, Georgia "Tiny" Broadwick became the first woman to parachute from an airplane.

To find out how old Georgia Broadwick was when she made her first parachute jump, finish each word that begins with the letters *para*. Use the Letter Bank and the definitions as clues. Then, unscramble the circled letters to finish the sentence below.

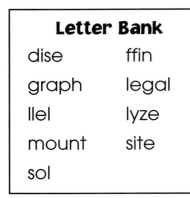

Letter Bank

dise	ffin
graph	legal
llel	lyze
mount	site
sol	

1. para __ __ Ⓞ __ : being the same distance apart at all points

2. para __ Ⓞ __ __ : a place of great happiness

3. para __ __ __ : a small umbrella

4. para __ __ __ __ __ : a group of sentences about the same idea

5. para ⓄⓄ __ __ : a white substance like wax

6. para __ __ __ Ⓞ __ : above all others, very important

7. para __ __ __ __ : to take away the power to move

8. para __ Ⓞ __ __ __ : a professional who assists a lawyer

9. para __ __ Ⓞ __ : an organism living in or on another organism

Tiny was __ __ __ __ __ __ years old!

Pig Punch Line

National Pig Day takes place during the first week of March. Other words for a pig are hog and swine. These words are synonyms.

Write a synonym for each clue. Then, use the number code to answer the riddle below.

___ ___ ___ boy
    5

___ ___ ___ ___ boat
      7

___ ___ ___ ___ person
4

___ ___ ___ ___ ___ author
1

___ ___ ___ ___ ___ pupil
  3

___ ___ ___ ___ ___ ___ doctor
9

___ ___ ___ ___ ___ instructor
   10

___ ___ ___ ___ ___ baby
2

___ ___ ___ ___ rabbit
    11

___ ___ ___ ___ horse
6

___ ___ ___ insect
   8

How do pigs write?

___ ___ ___ ___   ___   ___ ___ ___ ___ ___ ___ ___
1 2 3 4   5   6 7 8 9 10 11

Name _____

Phone a Friend

On March 10, 1876, Alexander Graham Bell spoke the first words over a telephone.

To find out what he said, write the homophone for each word. Then, use the number code to complete the telephone message.

1. hare

13	4	17	2

2. ewe

22	10	24

3. their

21		14	15	

4. one

3	7	8

5. pain

		20	12

6. choose

9			18	6

7. meet

11		19	5

8. know

	23

9. mail

1			16

"	1	2	.		3	4	5	6	7	8	,
9	10	11	12		13	14	15	16	.		17
18	19	20	21		22	23	24	!	"		

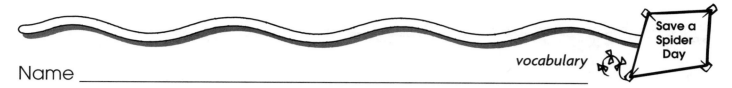

Name _____

Eight Useful Legs

March 14 is Save a Spider Day. There are more than 30,000 kinds of spiders. Because spiders eat harmful insects, they are helpful to people.

Use the definitions and letter clues to complete each spider puzzle.

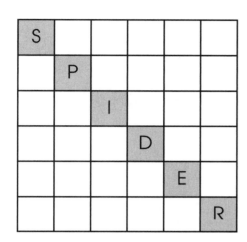

1. to look for something
2. opposite of closed
3. ten less than forty
4. a seat on a horse
5. piece of equipment used in tennis
6. top of a pencil, used to remove marks

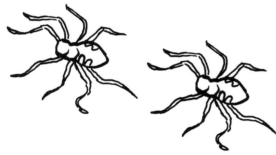

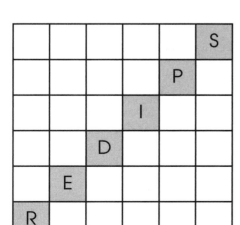

7. break time during school
8. to take something that is given
9. missing a pitch in baseball
10. halfway between two things
11. the distance from one end to the other end
12. a prize

Name _____

Try This!

A shamrock is the national symbol of Ireland. It has three leaves and is often worn on March 17, St. Patrick's Day.

Tri is a prefix that means "three." Use the grid to complete each word with the prefix *tri*. The first coordinate given is from the horizontal row of letters.

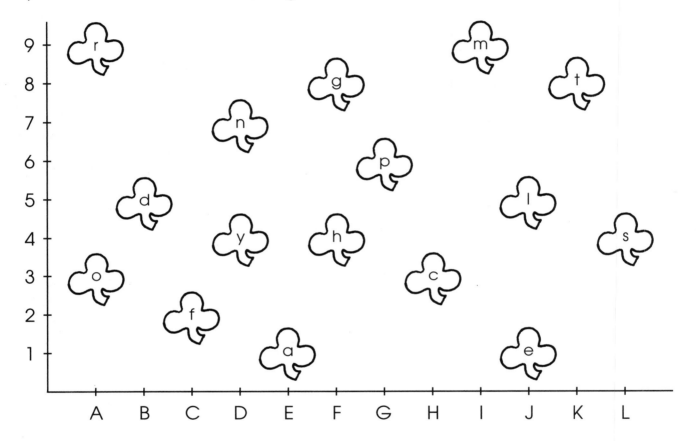

1. tri ___ ___ ___ ___ ___
(E, 1) (D, 7) (F, 8) (J, 5) (J, 1)

2. tri ___ ___ ___ ___
(H, 3) (J, 1) (G, 6) (L, 4)

3. tri ___ ___ ___ ___
(J, 5) (A, 3) (F, 8) (D, 4)

4. tri ___ ___ ___ ___
(G, 6) (J, 5) (J, 1) (K, 8)

5. tri ___ ___ ___ ___ ___
(H, 3) (D, 4) (H, 3) (J, 5) (J, 1)

6. tri ___ ___ ___
(G, 6) (A, 3) (B, 5)

7. tri ___ ___ ___ ___ ___ ___
(E, 1) (K, 8) (F, 4) (J, 5) (A, 3) (D, 7)

8. tri ___ ___ ___ ___ ___
(C, 2) (A, 3) (H, 3) (E, 1) (J, 5)

9. tri ___ ___ ___
(G, 6) (J, 5) (J, 1)

10. tri ___ ___ ___ ___ ___ ___
(I, 9) (J, 1) (L, 4) (K, 8) (J, 1) (A, 9)

Word Games: Grades 3–4

Name _____

Sports Scoop

Did you know that a peach basket was used as the first basketball hoop? Learn more interesting facts during National Sports Trivia Week celebrated in the middle of March.

Which president played football for the University of Michigan? To find out, unscramble each sport. Then, write the letter from each shaded box in order on the lines below to spell this president's name.

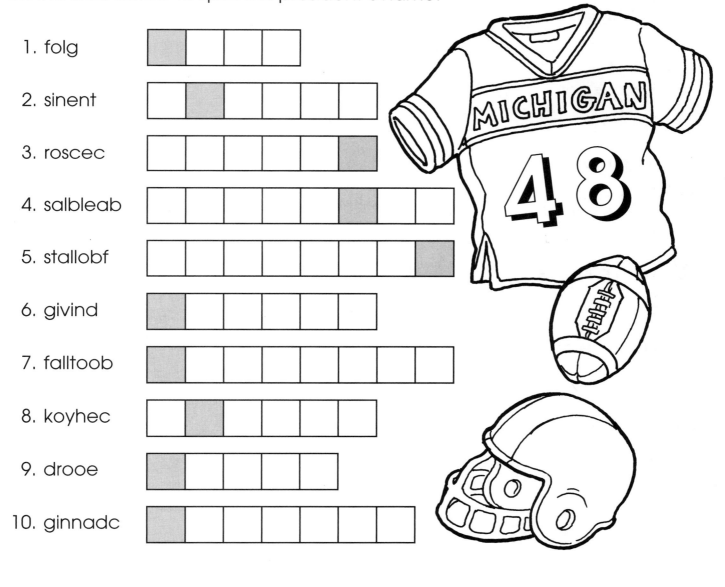

1. folg

2. sinent

3. roscec

4. salbleab

5. stallobf

6. givind

7. falltoob

8. koyhec

9. drooe

10. ginnadc

President ___ ___ ___ ___ ___ ___   ___ ___ ___

Name _____

Time to Clean

March 20 or 21 marks the first day of spring. Traditionally, spring is a time for cleaning.

"Clean" each word by crossing out the letter that does not belong. Then, write the crossed-out letters in order on the blanks below to finish the fact about another popular spring activity.

1. e k x c i t e d
2. p i c i n i c
3. e m e r g e n t c y
4. t o m a t o e
5. r e s c e i v e
6. c a r r o o t
7. v o l l u n t e e r
8. g r e e d d y
9. s k i n n e y
10. n e c s e s s a r y
11. f o r t t y
12. e n o u f g h
13. g a l l o o n
14. l e a r r n
15. i m m p r o v e
16. d e s c i m a l
17. m a m m a a l
18. f i r i e n d
19. n e a r r e s t
20. p l e a s c u r e
21. o u r r s e l v e s
22. f i n a l l a y
23. l e a f v e s
24. c o n t t i n u e

___ ___ ___ ___ ___   are the   ___ ___ ___ ___ ___ ___   ___ ___ ___ ___ ___ ___

of ___ ___ ___ ___ ___ ___ ___ ___ ___.

A Number of Words

April is Mathematics Education Month.

Complete the crossword puzzle with mathematic vocabulary. Then, unscramble the shaded letters to answer the riddle below.

Across

1. a three-sided figure

4. repeated addition

6. no amount

8. the answer to an addition problem

9. Examples are 3, 5, and 7.

10. taking away one number from another

11. showing how many times one number contains another number

Down

1. ten times a hundred

2. Examples are 2, 4, and 6.

3. one thousand times one million

5. the distance around a figure

7. a part of a whole

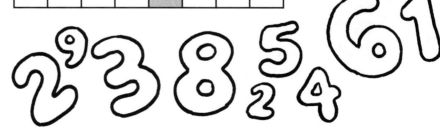

Why was the math book unhappy?

It had too many __ __ __ __ __ __ __ __!

April Fools' Day

Time to Fool

April 1 is April Fools' Day. On this day in France, a person tries to pin a paper fish on someone else's back without getting caught.

Oops! All the baby animals got mixed up. Use the code to write each baby's name. Then, draw a line to match it to its mother.

a	b	c	d	e	f	g	h	i	k	l	m	n	o	p	r	s	t	u	v	w
✿	☞	✓	✕	✚	✌	✳	★	✂	✳	✈	○	■	↗	➌	➤	✍	▲	◆	❖	☞

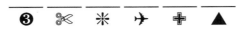

Word Games: Grades 3–4

A Journey to the Top

On April 6, 1909, it is believed that Robert E. Peary became the first person to reach the North Pole. The *U.S.S. Nautilus* was the first submarine to travel under the Arctic ice to the pole.

Complete the puzzle using words that have to do with cold. Then, write the letter in each shaded box in order on the blanks below to learn Robert Peary's rank in the navy.

1. a frozen dessert made from milk products

2. carries people over the snow

3. a polar bear is this type of animal

4. a black-and-white bird that cannot fly

5. a sport played on ice wearing skates

6. a large piece of floating ice from a glacier

7. a hut built from blocks of snow

8. a heavy snowstorm

9. a hanging piece of pointed ice

_ _ _ _ _ _ _ _ Robert E. Peary

Name _____

Space Flight

On April 12, 1961, Russian Yuri Gagarin became the first man to travel into space.

Man, space, and spacecraft are all nouns. Man is a person, space is a place, and spacecraft is a thing. Using the clues, write a noun that begins with each letter of Yuri Gagarin's name. To find out what Russian astronauts are called, use the number code to complete the following sentence.

Yuri Gagarin was a

___ ___ ___ ___ ___ ___ ___ ___ ___.
1   2   3   4   5   6   7   8   9

Y		¹		
U	⁶			
R				
I				
G		⁵		
A	⁹			
G				⁴
A			²	
R	⁸			
I			⁷	
N			³	

1. (thing) a large boat

2. (person) the brother of a father or mother

3. (place) a large stream of water

4. (thing) frosting

5. (thing) round ball with a map of the world

6. (thing) a reference book of maps

7. (person) a man getting married

8. (person) a performer

9. (thing) used to measure inches

10. (place) country in southern Europe

11. (thing) a loud sound

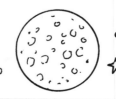

America's First Elephant

Elephant Excitement

On April 13, 1796, America's first elephant arrived in New York. It came from Bengal, India.

Elephants are a popular attraction at zoos. Follow the other popular zoo animals listed through the maze. The letters go forward, backward, up, and down.

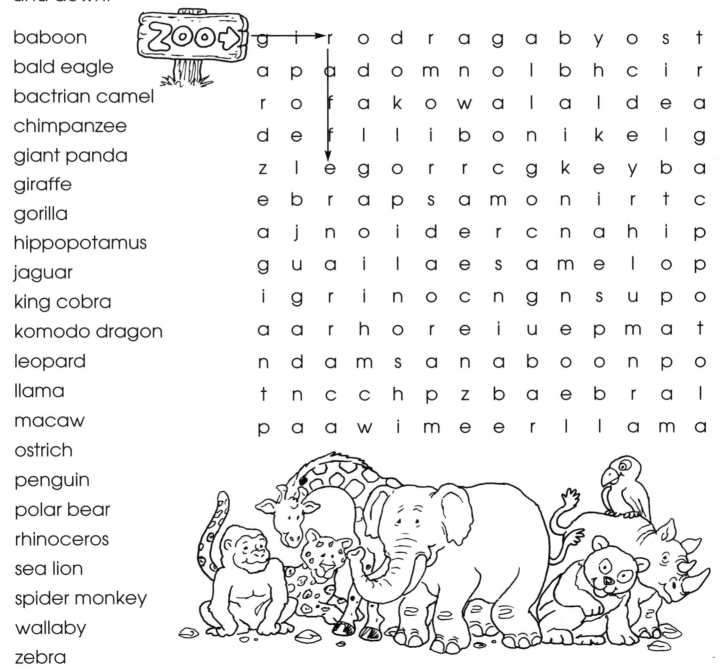

baboon
bald eagle
bactrian camel
chimpanzee
giant panda
giraffe
gorilla
hippopotamus
jaguar
king cobra
komodo dragon
leopard
llama
macaw
ostrich
penguin
polar bear
rhinoceros
sea lion
spider monkey
wallaby
zebra

```
g  i  r  o  d  r  a  g  a  b  y  o  s  t
a  p  a  d  o  m  n  o  l  b  h  c  i  r
r  o  f  a  k  o  w  a  l  a  l  d  e  a
d  e  f  l  l  i  b  o  n  i  k  e  l  g
z  l  e  g  o  r  r  c  g  k  e  y  b  a
e  b  r  a  p  s  a  m  o  n  i  r  t  c
a  j  n  o  i  d  e  r  c  n  a  h  i  p
g  u  a  i  l  a  e  s  a  m  e  l  o  p
i  g  r  i  n  o  c  n  g  n  s  u  p  o
a  a  r  h  o  r  e  i  u  e  p  m  a  t
n  d  a  m  s  a  n  a  b  o  o  n  p  o
t  n  c  c  h  p  z  b  a  e  b  r  a  l
p  a  a  w  i  m  e  e  r  l  l  a  m  a
```

Word Games: Grades 3–4

Name _____

The British Are Coming!

On the evening of April 18, 1775, Paul Revere made his famous midnight ride to warn the colonists of the invading British troops.

Paul Revere's ride happened in the past. Fit the past tense of each verb into its puzzle. Then, use the number code to finish the sentence below about Paul Revere and his men.

1. feed
   ride
   sell

2. hold
   make
   read

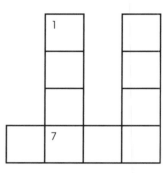

3. bring
   build
   stand

4. hang
   have
   win

They were called __ __ __ __ __ __ __ __ __ because they had to be
              1 2 3 4 5 6 1 7 3

ready to fight at a __ __ __ __ __ __ ' __ notice.
                   1 2 3 4 5 6   8

Name _____

Huffing and Puffing

The first running of the Boston Marathon was held on April 19, 1897.

To find out how far this race is, complete each puzzle by writing a word that completes each sentence using the letter clue in the puzzle. Then, use the code to discover the answer.

A marathon is ___ ___ ___ ___ ___ ___ - ___ ___ ___ miles long!
         1   2   3   4   5   6   7   8   9

The boy was hiding _____ the chair.

Abraham Lincoln was a very _____ man.

Because Kelly was ill, she was _____ from school.

Please be very _____ with the kitten.

A rattlesnake has _____ in its bite.

Tell me the _____ you are late.

Mr. Rosman was elected _____ of our town.

There are _____ seconds in a minute.

I cannot _____ you to go until your work is finished.

Luis showed his _____ by stomping is feet.

Always look both ways before you _____ the street.

Name _____

Save Our Planet

April 22 is Earth Day. It is a day set aside for all to become aware of the need to preserve the environment.

Find each word in the Word Bank in the puzzle. The words go forward, backward, up, down, and diagonally. Then, write the remaining letters on the blanks to find out when Earth Day began.

___ ___ ___ ___ ___ ___   ___ ___ ___   ___ ___ ___   ___ ___ ___ ___ ___

___ ___ ___ ___ ___ ___ ___ ___ ___   ___ ___   ___ ___ ___   ___ ___ ___ ___

___ ___ ___ ___ ___ ___ ___ ___   ___ ___ ___ ___ ___ ___ ___ ___ ___ .

Word Bank

atmosphere
continent
crust
desert
glacier
inner core
mantle
minerals
mountain
ocean
outer core
plain
plateau
river
soil
valley
tributary

```
m  e  a  r  y  r  a  t  u  b  i  r  t
i  n  n  e  r  c  o  r  e  t  h  e
n  d  a  o  v  n  i  a  l  p  n  y  r
e  w  a  c  c  a  s  f  i  r  e  s  o
r  m  t  e  r  o  l  b  s  e  n  r  c
a  o  a  a  u  r  g  l  a  c  i  e  r
l  u  v  n  s  o  i  l  e  e  t  v  e
s  n  d  i  t  n  t  h  e  y  n  i  t
y  t  e  a  r  l  n  i  n  e  o  r  u
t  a  p  l  a  t  e  a  u  e  c  e  o
n  i  s  e  v  e  n  t  r  e  s  e  d
t  n  y  a  t  m  o  s  p  h  e  r  e
```

Samuel F. Morse's Birthday

Name _____

Ways to Communicate

Samuel F. Morse was born on April 27, 1791. He invented the Morse code, which changed the way people would communicate around the world.

Fill in each blank using the Morse code to learn the year other communication inventions were invented.

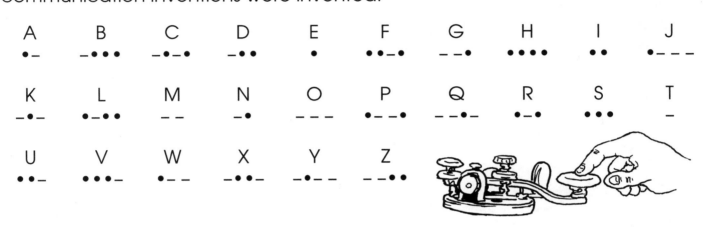

A	B	C	D	E	F	G	H	I	J
•—	—•••	—•—•	—••	•	••—•	——•	••••	••	•———

K	L	M	N	O	P	Q	R	S	T
—•—	•—••	——	—•	———	•——•	——•—	•—•	•••	—

U	V	W	X	Y	Z
••—	•••—	•——	—••—	—•——	——••

1. 1867 ___ ___ ___ ___ ___ ___ ___ ___ ___ ___
   — —•—• •—• • •—— •—• •• — • •—•

2. 1876 ___ ___ ___ ___ ___ ___ ___ ___ ___
   — • •—•• • •——• •••• ——— —• •

3. 1888 ___ ___ ___ ___ ___ ___ ___ ___ ___ ___ ___
   —••• •— •—•• •—•• •——• ——— •• —• — •——• • —•

4. 1947 ___ ___ ___ ___ ___ ___ ___ ___ ___
   — •—• •— —• ••• •• ••• — ——— •—•

5. 1965 ___ ___ ___ ___ ___ ___ ___ ___ ___ ___ ___ ___
   •—— ——— •—• —•• •——• •—• ——— —•—• • ••• ••• ——— •—•

6. 1987 ___ ___ ___ ___ ___ ___ ___ ___ ___ ___ ___ ___ ___ ___
   •—•• •— •—•• — ——— •—• —•—• ——— —— •——• ••— — • •—•

7. 1994 ___ ___ ___ ___ ___ ___ ___ ___ ___ ___ ___ ___
   —•• •• —•— •• — •— •—•• —•—• •— —— • •—• •—

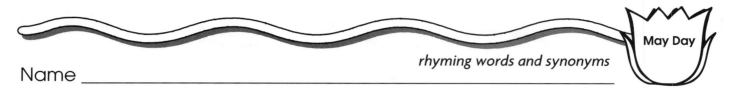

Name _____

Rhyme Time

May Day is a spring festival celebrated on May 1. Often children dance around a maypole and hang baskets filled with candy and flowers on doorknobs.

Use the synonym clues to complete each flower with two rhyming words.

1. robber
   leader

2. flunk
   prison

3. complain
   eat

4. cloudy
   inactive

5. collision
   garbage

6. fortune
   weigh

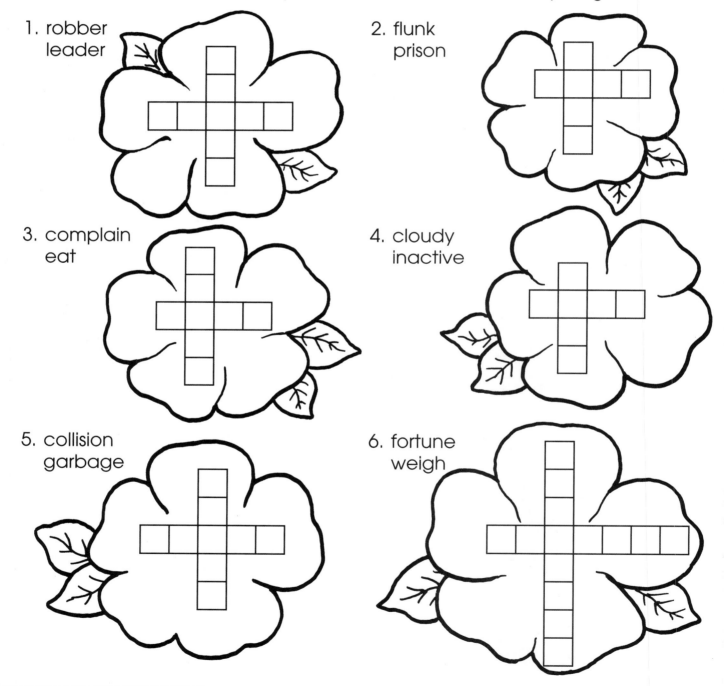

Name _____

Play It Again

National Music Week begins the first Sunday in May.

Fit the name of each musical instrument from the Word Bank in the puzzle. Use the letters *m, u, s, i,* and *c* as clues.

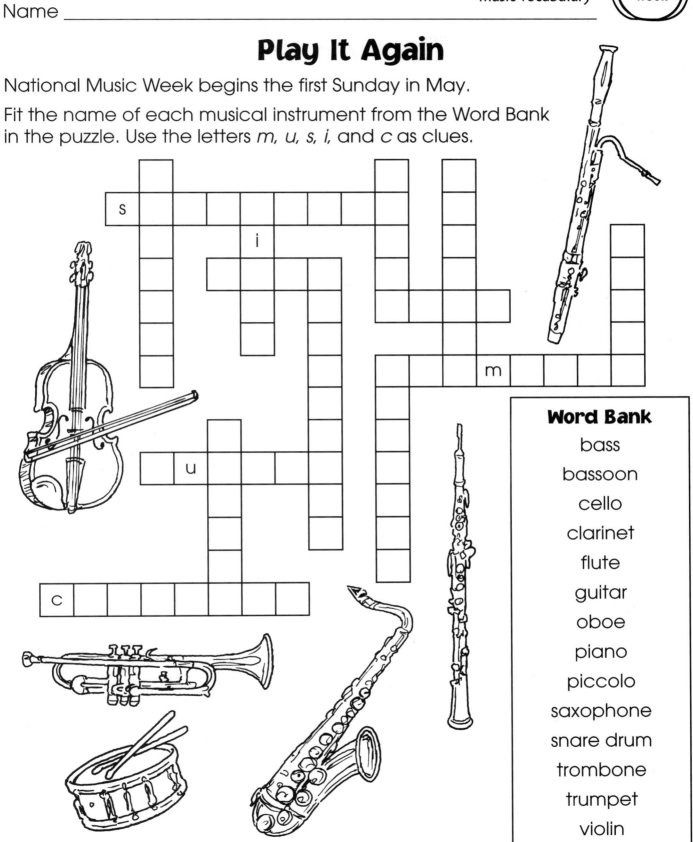

Word Bank

bass
bassoon
cello
clarinet
flute
guitar
oboe
piano
piccolo
saxophone
snare drum
trombone
trumpet
violin

81

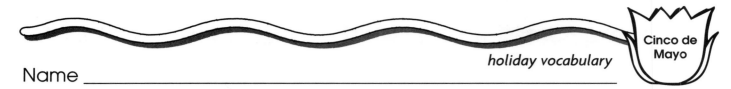

Name _____

Festival Fun

Cinco de Mayo is a Mexican holiday celebrated on May 5. Many Americans also celebrate this holiday.

To find out more about Cinco de Mayo, complete each sentence using the grid. The first coordinate given is from the horizontal row of letters.

1. A Mexican festival is called a ___ ___ ___ ___ ___ ___.
   (J, 6) (J, 1) (L, 2) (K, 4) (D, 6) (B, 7)

2. This holiday honors the ___ ___ ___ ___ ___ ___ ___ ___ ___ of the city
   (F, 2) (J, 1) (N, 3) (N, 3) (B, 7) (C, 1) (L, 2) (B, 3) (K, 4)

   of ___ ___ ___ ___ ___ ___ who fought the invading French army.
   (H, 7) (I, 3) (L, 2) (H, 5) (N, 3) (B, 7)

3. Children often play the ___ ___ ___ ___ ___ ___ game.
   (H, 7) (J, 1) (L, 7) (B, 7) (D, 6) (B, 7)

4. ___ ___ ___ ___ ___ ___ ___ ___ bands play music.
   (A, 5) (B, 7) (B, 3) (J, 1) (B, 7) (E, 4) (M, 5) (J, 1)

5. It is also a time to ___ ___ ___ ___ ___. Many different foods are served
   (J, 6) (L, 2) (B, 7) (K, 4) (D, 6)

   including ___ ___ ___ ___ ___ ___ ___ ___ ___.
   (D, 6) (N, 1) (B, 3) (D, 6) (J, 1) (N, 3) (N, 3) (B, 7) (K, 4)

Name _____

The Mighty Mississippi

In May of 1541, a group of explorers discovered the Mississippi River. They were searching for gold. Discover and search are action verbs.

Write an action verb in the puzzle for each sentence. The last letter of each word is the first letter of the next word. Some letters of the puzzle have been given. To discover the leader's name, use the code to fill in the blanks.

1. Juan will _____ you to the treasure.

2. You should _____ water when you are thirsty.

3. I _____ the answer to the problem.

4. Tomorrow, Kristen will _____ Jack a letter.

5. We must _____ the entire cave.

6. The family will _____ dinner at six o'clock.

7. Lisa, please _____ me the ball.

8. We will _____ the movie again tomorrow.

9. Trent will _____ his dad rake the leaves.

10. Jill will _____ the grocery cart for her mom.

11. Sam likes to _____ behind the sofa.

Name _____

A World of Moms

Mother's Day is celebrated on the second Sunday in May. President Woodrow Wilson made this a national celebration on May 9, 1914.

Use the picture code to write *mother* in many different languages.

Picture Code

Letter	
a	
d	
e	
è	
i	
k	
l	
m	
o	
r	
t	
u	
μ	
α	
ᵗ	
ι	
τ	

Czech
_ _   _ _ _ _ _

Dutch
_ _   _ _ _ _ _ _

French
_ _   _ _ _ _

German
_ _ _   _ _ _ _ _ _
 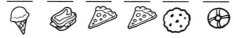

Greek
_ _ _ _

Italian
_ _   _ _ _ _ _

Japanese
_ _ _ _

Spanish
_ _ _ _ _

Word Games: Grades 3–4

Name _____

analogies

A Sour Treat

International Pickle Week is celebrated in the middle of May. Pickles are made from cucumbers.

To answer the riddle below, complete each analogy with a word that ends in *le* using the letter clues. Then, use the picture code to fill in the blanks below.

1. Geese is to goose as [c ❀ _ _ _ _] is to cow.

2. Drop is to baseball as [◆ u _ _ _ _] is to football.

3. Horse is to stable as [c ⊶ _ _ _ _] is to knight.

4. Aunt is to woman as [u _ _ ✖ _] is to man.

5. Front is to forward as [m _ ○ _ _ _] is to center.

6. Party is to friend as [b _ _ _ ▮] is to enemy.

7. Boring is to thrilling as [e _ _ ⇨ _ _ _] is to wonderful.

8. Basket is to kitten as [r _ ✧ _ _] is to baby.

What is a crazy pickle?

___ ___ ___ ___ ___ y ___ ___ ___ ___ !
⊶   ○ ❀ ◆ ◆   ✧ ⇨ ✖ ▮

© Carson-Dellosa CD-4331   **85**   Word Games: Grades 3–4

Name _____

Clara Barton

On May 21, 1881, the American Red Cross was formed. Its first president was Clara Barton. Clara Barton helped hundreds of soldiers during the Civil War.

To find out what Clara Barton was called, circle each word from the Word Bank in the puzzle. The words will go forward, backward, up, down, and diagonally. Then, write the remaining letters in order on the blanks below.

Word Bank

ambitious	author	brave	courageous
fearless	generous	heroic	intelligent
lecturer	nurse	president	teacher

```
t c l a t q i m i d c t
n a r a e b a r t o o n
e u n w a a b s f k u e
d t r n c i o r e h r g
i h o s h w n a a s a i
s o t h e e a n r v g l
e r g e r l o f l t e l
r h s u o r e n e g o e
p e b a t t l e s f u t
a m b i t i o u s i s n
e l l e c t u r e r d i
```

___ ___ ___ ___   ___ ___ ___ ___ ___ ___   ___ ___ ___

___ ___ ___ ___ ___ ___ ___ ___ ___ ___ ___ ___

___ ___ ___ ___ ___ ___ ___ ___ ___ ___ ___ ___ ___ .

Name _____

A Day for Remembering

Memorial Day is observed on the last Monday in May. It was originally a day to honor those who died in the Civil War. Today, this holiday also honors all who have died in any war while serving the United States.

To find out another name for Memorial Day, write the antonym for each word using the letter clue. Then, use the number code to write the letters on the blanks below.

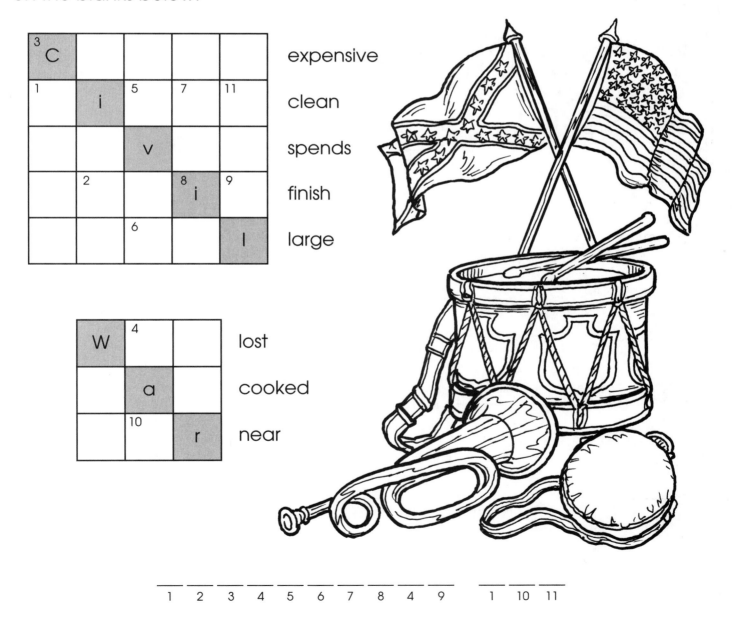

expensive

clean

spends

finish

large

lost

cooked

near

___ ___ ___ ___ ___ ___ ___ ___ ___ ___ ___ ___ ___
1   2   3   4   5   6   7   8   4   9   1   10 11

Name _____

Hail a Cab

On May 31, 1907, the first taxis went into service.

To find out what city these cabs came to, unscramble each word. Each word has the letters *C*, *A*, and *B* in it. Use the pictures in the box as clues. Then, use the number code to write the city on the blanks below.

1. cabr   __ __ __ __
                    6

2. cabno   __ __ __ __ __
                       5

3. cabynol   __ __ __ __ __ __ __
                             11

4. cabni   __ __ __ __ __
                    9

5. cabydrak   __ __ __ __ __ __ __
                   7 4

6. cabontrutis __ __ __ __ __ __ __ __ __ __
                            10   1

7. cabhe   __ __ __ __ __
                 2   8

8. cabrawdk   __ __ __ __ __ __ __
                       3

__ __ __   __ __ __ __   __ __ __ __
 1 2 3   4 5 6 7   8 9 10 11

Name _____

Rolling Down the River

June is American Rivers Month. The place where a river begins is the source of the river. The place where a river empties into another body of water is the mouth of the river.

Start at the source of the puzzle. Follow the names of American rivers listed in the River Bank to the mouth of the puzzle. The names of the rivers will go forward, backward, up, and down.

River Bank

Arkansas
Colorado
Hudson
Mississippi
Missouri
Niagara
Ohio
Platte
Potomac
Rio Grande
Sacramento
Shenandoah
Snake
Suwannee
Tennessee
Yellowstone
Yukon
Wabash

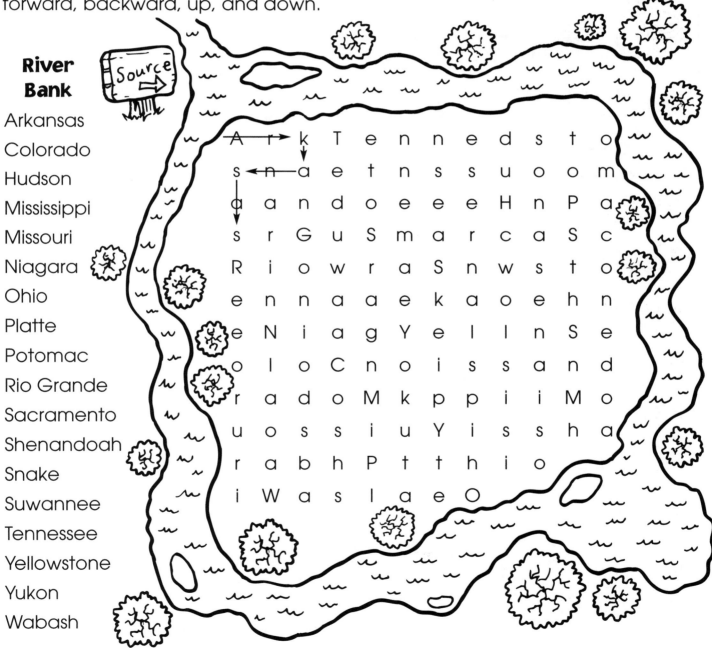

Name _____

Flying Proud

The first flag of the United States was adopted by the Continental Congress in 1777. This event is now celebrated as Flag Day on June 14.

To learn more about the flags of other places around the world, write the places from the Word Bank in the puzzle. Use the given letters *f, l, a,* and *g* as clues. After the puzzle is complete, write the name of the country below its flag on page 91.

Word Bank

Australia	Denmark	Honduras	Scotland
Canada	France	Japan	Uruguay
Chile	Greece	Norway	
China	Greenland	Panama	

Name _____

Across

1.

_____

5.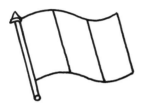

_____

7.

_____

8.

_____

9.

_____

10.

_____

Down

12.

_____

1.

_____

2.

_____

3.

_____

4.

_____

6.

_____

9.

_____

11.

_____

Summer Fun

Summer begins when the summer solstice occurs. This happens on June 20 or 21. On this day, there are more hours of daylight than any other day of the year.

Summer is a time for fun! Complete each sentence below with a word about summer. Then, find each word in the puzzle on page 93. The words will go forward, backward, up, down, and diagonally.

1. Grab your racket, and let's go play __ __ __ __ __ __.

2. Mom packed a basket with food for our __ __ __ __ __ __.

3. We are taking a __ __ __ __ __ __ __ __ to the Grand Canyon.

4. Carrie is riding her __ __ __ __ __ __ __ to the park.

5. Mark hit a home run at the __ __ __ __ __ __ __ __ __ game.

6. We will cool off at the __ __ __ __ __ __ __ __ __ pool.

7. Summer begins in the month of __ __ __ __.

8. On __ __ __ __ 4, there will be a celebration.

9. __ __ __ __ __ __ __ is the last full month of summer.

10. It is fun to spit seeds from a __ __ __ __ __ __ __ __ __ __ __ __ !

11. Ann picked a red juicy __ __ __ __ __ __ __ __ __ __ __ __ from the garden.

12. The Wilhelm family likes to __ __ __ __ __ __ to California during the summer.

13. We tried to catch a __ __ __ __ __ __ __ __ __ last night.

14. There are no clouds, just lots of __ __ __ __ __ __ __ __ __ __.

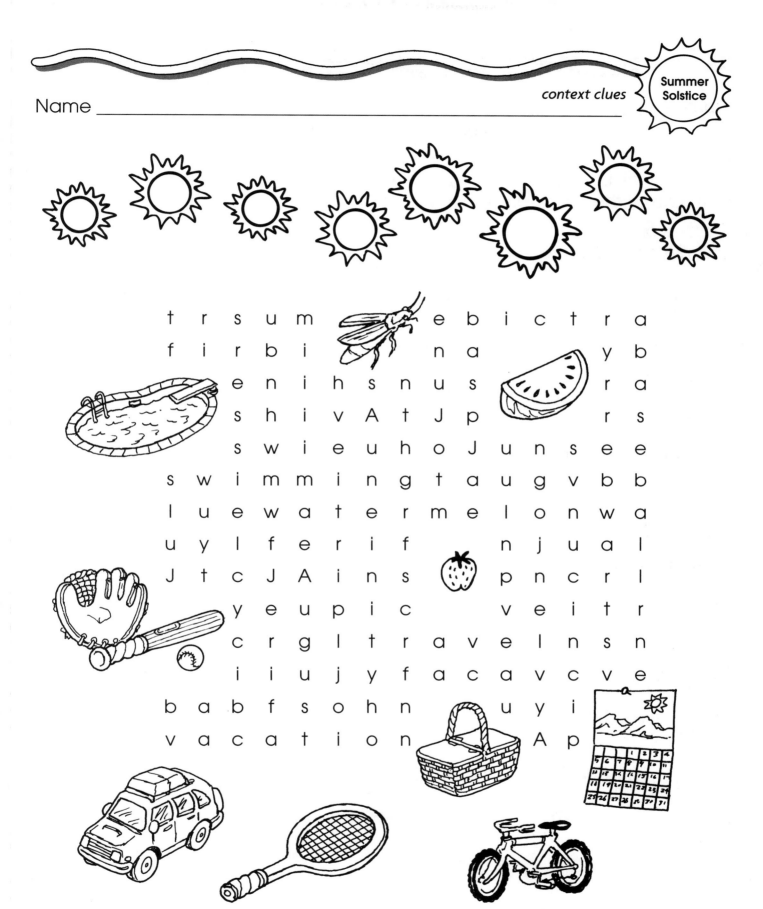

Name _____

A Perfect Pop

Father's Day is the third Sunday in June. A father has more than one job. Try to name all the things a father may do.

Many words have more than one meaning. Write the word that has the two given meanings. Then, use the number code to answer the riddle below.

1. to make a journey | 11 | | 17 | | to cause someone to fall

2. a band around a finger | | | 2 | 9 | a telephone sound

3. to go down below the surface | | 1 | 18 | | a basin to hold water

4. to fasten | | 8 | | 15 | a sea lion

5. a shape that has five points | 5 | | 12 | | an actor who plays the leading role

6. to release | | | 21 | 6 | no charge for something

7. bag for carrying things on your back | | 4 | 3 | | to place in something for storing

8. to demonstrate | | 13 | 10 | | a performance

9. the manager | | 19 | | | to give orders

10. hard growth on the head of some animals | 7 | 14 | | 20 | used to make a loud warning sound

11. to relax or sleep | | 16 | | | something that is left

Why did the golfer need two pairs of pants?

___ ___   ___ ___ ___ ___   ___ ___   ___ ___ ___ ___ ___   ___ ___ ___ ___
1   2   3   4   5   6   7   8   9   10 11 12 13   14 15 16

___ ___   ___ ___ ___!
17 18   19 20 21

94

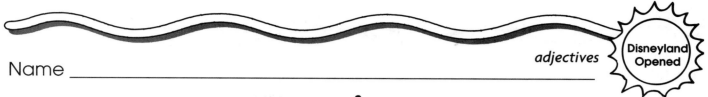

The Happiest Place

In July of 1955, Disneyland opened in California. Disneyland is known as "the happiest place on Earth."

Happiest is an adjective. It describes the noun "place." Using the definition clues, write an adjective that begins with each letter in Disneyland. Then, use the code to write the name of the city in which this park is located.

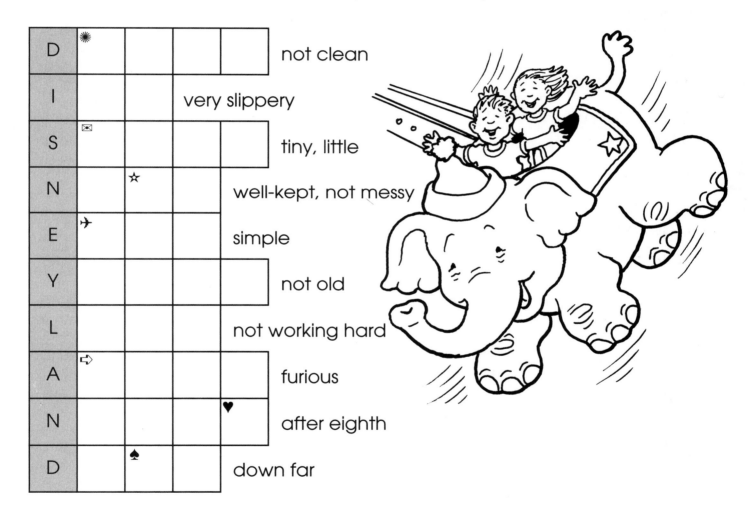

D	☀				not clean
I					very slippery
S	✉				tiny, little
N		☆			well-kept, not messy
E	✈				simple
Y					not old
L					not working hard
A	⇨				furious
N			♥		after eighth
D		♠			down far

Disneyland is located in __ __ __ __ __ __ __, California.

       ☆ ⇨ ✈ ♥ ♠ ☀ ✉

Name _____

Light up the Sky

The United States celebrates its independence on July 4. Spectacular celebrations occur across the country.

Many other important events have also taken place on July 4. To learn about one of them, unscramble the words about this holiday. Use the pictures as clues. Then, use the number code to complete the sentence below.

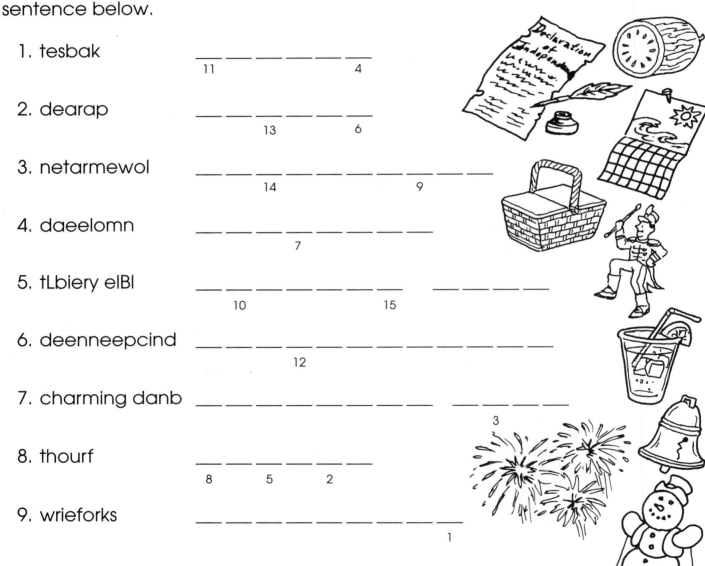

1. tesbak
   __ __ __ __ __ __
   11   4

2. dearap
   __ __ __ __ __ __
      13   6

3. netarmewol
   __ __ __ __ __ __ __ __ __
      14   9

4. daeelomn
   __ __ __ __ __ __ __
         7

5. tLbiery elBl
   __ __ __ __ __ __ __ __ __ __ __
      10   15

6. deenneepcind
   __ __ __ __ __ __ __ __ __ __ __ __
         12

7. charming danb
   __ __ __ __ __ __ __ __ __ __ __ __

8. thourf
   __ __ __ __ __ __
   8 5 2

9. wrieforks
   __ __ __ __ __ __ __ __ __
                        1

On July 4, 1884, France presented this to the United States:

the __ __ __ __ __ __ __ __ __ __ __ __ __ __ __
    1 2 3 4 5 6   7 8   9 10 11 12 13 14 15

America's First 18-Hole Golf Course

Chip and Putt

July 18 is the anniversary of the first 18-hole golf course in America. It was built in Wheaton, Illinois, in 1893.

Chip and putt are two actions a golfer does. Complete each puzzle with an action verb using the sentence clues.

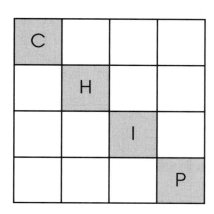

1. Connor needs to _____ his hair.

2. I will _____ some wood for a fire.

3. The boat must _____ across the ocean.

4. The girls are going to hop, _____, and jump around the playground.

5. Kristen likes to _____ the grocery cart.

6. Let's go _____ on the trampoline.

7. Claire took a _____ of the apple.

8. Every night the cats _____ for mice.

97

Name _____

A Giant Leap

"That's one small step for a man, one giant leap for mankind." These are the famous words spoken by the first man to walk on the moon. This historic event happened on July 20, 1969.

To find out this man's name, use the definition clues and the words from the Word Bank to complete the path to the moon. Not all the words in the Word Bank will be used. Then, write the letters from each shaded box in order on the blanks below.

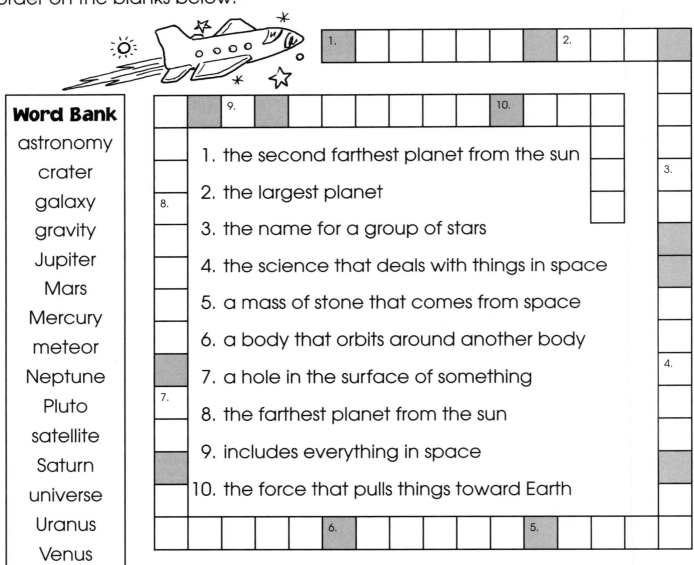

Word Bank

astronomy
crater
galaxy
gravity
Jupiter
Mars
Mercury
meteor
Neptune
Pluto
satellite
Saturn
universe
Uranus
Venus

1. the second farthest planet from the sun
2. the largest planet
3. the name for a group of stars
4. the science that deals with things in space
5. a mass of stone that comes from space
6. a body that orbits around another body
7. a hole in the surface of something
8. the farthest planet from the sun
9. includes everything in space
10. the force that pulls things toward Earth

___ ___ ___ ___   ___ ___ ___ ___ ___ ___

Watermelon Day

Name _____

Sweet and Juicy

August 3 is National Watermelon Day. Early explorers used watermelons as canteens.

To learn another interesting fact about this delicious fruit, write an antonym for each word using the letter clues. Then, use the code to complete the sentence below.

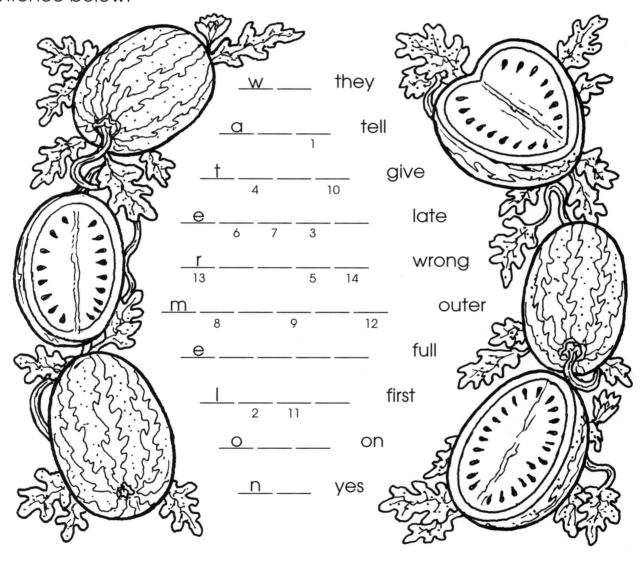

w ___ ___   they

a ___ ___   tell
$\quad$ 1

t ___ ___ ___   give
$\quad$ 4 $\quad$ 10

e ___ ___ ___ ___   late
$\quad$ 6 $\quad$ 7 $\quad$ 3

r ___ ___ ___ ___   wrong
13 $\quad$ 5 $\quad$ 14

m ___ ___ ___ ___   outer
$\quad$ 8 $\quad$ 9 $\quad$ 12

e ___ ___ ___   full

l ___ ___ ___   first
$\quad$ 2 $\quad$ 11

o ___ ___   on

n ___   yes

The ___ ___ ___ ___ ___ ___ ___ ___   ___ ___ ___ ___ ___ ___
$\quad$ 1 $\;$ 2 $\;$ 3 $\;$ 4 $\;$ 5 $\;$ 6 $\;$ 7 $\;$ 8 $\qquad$ 9 $\;$ 10 $\;$ 11 $\;$ 12 $\;$ 13 $\;$ 14

is the birthplace of watermelon.

Name _____

Clowning Around

The first week of August is International Clown Week. Clowns have been around for hundreds of years. They have also been called jesters, buffoons, and Joeys.

For each definition, write two rhyming words with the same vowel sound as in clown.

1. a circular noise   _____ _____

2. a city dress   _____ _____

3. a yell of three strikes   _____ _____

4. a hurting sofa   _____ _____

5. a rodent's residence   _____ _____

6. a pig's hit   _____ _____

7. a discovered beagle   _____ _____

8. a sad part of speech   _____ _____

9. white, fluffy noise   _____ _____

10. a right-away
    milking animal   _____ _____

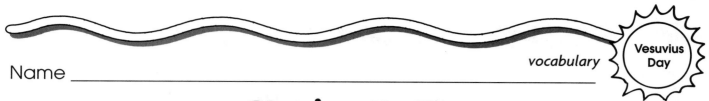

Blowing Its Top

Vesuvius is one of the world's most famous volcanoes. Its first recorded eruption occurred on August 24, 79 A.D.

To find out the country where this volcano is located, write a word for each definition using the letter clues. Then, use the code to write the country's name below.

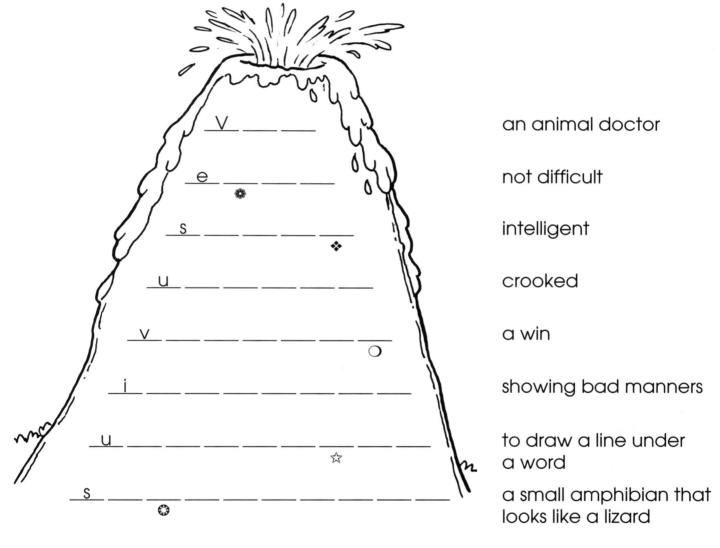

v _ _ _ _ _ — an animal doctor

e _ ✽ _ _ _ — not difficult

s _ _ _ _ ✦ — intelligent

u _ _ _ _ _ _ — crooked

v _ _ _ _ ○ — a win

i _ _ _ _ _ _ — showing bad manners

u _ _ _ _ _ ☆ _ — to draw a line under a word

s _ ✹ _ _ _ _ _ _ _ — a small amphibian that looks like a lizard

Vesuvius is located in ___ ___ ___ ___ ___.
☆ ✦ ✽ ✹ ○

Fun Fact

Popping Hot

Once the farmers in Missouri had something funny happen to them because it was so hot.

To find out what happened, unscramble each word which has the letters *H, O,* and *T* in it. Use each sentence as a clue. Then, use the number code to fill in the blanks below.

1. HOTLPSAI   Madison went to the __ __ __ __ __ __ __ __ to get
$${}_{20}\ {}_{5}\ {}_{11}\ \ \ {}_{22}\ {}_{23}$$
her tonsils out.

2. HOTLE   When my family went to Chicago, we stayed in a
__ __ __ __ __ with 22 floors.
$${}_{6}\ \ {}_{8}$$

3. HOTWR   Jason, __ __ __ __ __ me the ball.
$${}_{17}\ \ {}_{3}$$

4. HOTS   Susan __ __ __ __ the arrow at the target.
$${}_{24}\ {}_{13}$$

5. HOTUFR   Alex was the __ __ __ __ __ __ person in line.
$${}_{16}\ {}_{15}\ \ {}_{10}$$

6. HOTMSTURREDN   The __ __ __ __ __ __ __ __ __ __ __ __ woke me
$${}_{4}\ {}_{9}\ {}_{19}\ \ \ \ {}_{21}$$
up last night.

7. HOTCU   Do not __ __ __ __ __ the pan because it is very hot.
$${}_{14}\ \ \ {}_{1}$$

8. HOTOP   Kayla brought a __ __ __ __ __ of her dog to school.
$${}_{7}\ {}_{18}$$

9. HOTGU   That was a __ __ __ __ __ test!
$${}_{2}\ \ {}_{12}$$

__ __ __ __   __ __ __ __ __   __ __ __ __ __ __   __ __ __
1 2 3 4   5 6 7 7 8 9   10 11 12 13 14 15 16 16

__ __ __   __ __ __ __ __ __ __ !
17 18 19 20 21 22 23 k 24

Flying Fun

Did you know that scientists are trying to teach one kind of endangered bird to migrate from Wisconsin to Florida by dressing a scientist in a bird costume? Did you also know that another kind of bird can actually sleep while it is flying?

To find out what kind of bird each is, use the clues to name other things that fly. Then, use the number code to write each kind of bird in the boxes below.

1. This type of bird lives on every continent except Antarctica. It rhymes with "talk."

$\underline{\hphantom{xx}}\ \underline{\hphantom{xx}}\ \underline{\hphantom{xx}}\ \underline{\hphantom{xx}}$
11   20   10

2. This person operates an aircraft.

$\underline{\hphantom{xx}}\ \underline{\hphantom{xx}}\ \underline{\hphantom{xx}}\ \underline{\hphantom{xx}}$
   15   2   7

3. This is what a group of birds is called.

$\underline{\hphantom{xx}}\ \underline{\hphantom{xx}}\ \underline{\hphantom{xx}}$
   12   18

4. Although this black and white bird cannot fly in the air, it can "fly" underwater.

22   16   21

5. This insect, which is the color of grass, can leap about 20 times the length of its body.

17   8   9   13   19

6. This allows a person to jump from an airplane safely.

14   1   4

7. This beautiful, winged insect begins its life as an egg and then hatches into a caterpillar.

3   5   6

An

1	2	3	4	5	6	7	8	9

can sleep while flying.

Scientists are teaching the

10	11	12	13	14	15	16	17

18	19	20	21	22

Name _____

What a Worm!

A blackbird in Britain hit the jackpot. It caught a very long worm.

To find out how long this worm was, use each definition clue to write a word with *or* in it. Then, use the number code to complete the fact below about the worm's length.

8	o	r		a place with strong walls
1	o	r	16	a painful spot
17		o	r	6 the points in a game
	15	o	r	7 not tall
		14	o	r a person who treats the sick or injured
	o	r	12	not interesting
	o	r	13	2 the first half of the day
	3			o r 11 to travel through newly found land
4		10	o	r 9 5 the one liked the best

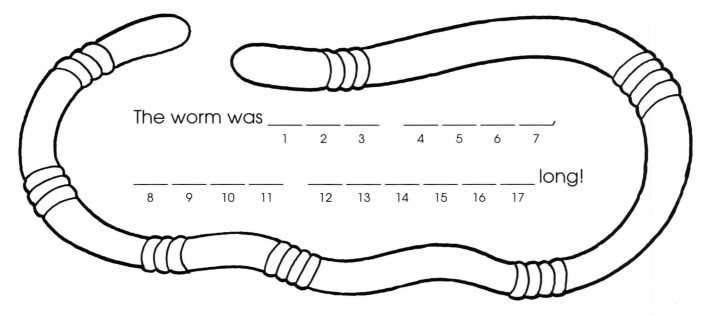

The worm was ___ ___ ___ ___ ___ ___ ___,

              1   2   3   4   5   6   7

___ ___ ___ ___ ___ ___ ___ ___ ___ ___ long!

  8   9   10   11   12   13   14   15   16   17

Time for Bed

Do you know what can sleep in dry weather without waking up?

To find out, use the picture clues to complete each puzzle with two words about sleep. Then, use the code to complete the sentence below about the super sleeper.

A _____ _____ _____ _____ _____
   ✗   ○   ➷   ✳   ◆

estivates, or sleeps, in dry weather until it rains.

Too Cool!

Do you know why Hollywood film stars started wearing sunglasses?

To find out, find each "cool" word from the Word Bank in the puzzle. The words will go forward, backward, up, down, and diagonally. Then, write the unused letters in order on the blanks below.

Word Bank

admirable
applause
awesome
choice
dazzling
fabulous
famous
glamorous
groovy
hip
incredible
marvelous
sensational
smart

```
s  u  o  m  a  f  a  c  t  o  r  s  d  i  d
n  m  l  o  t  i  n  c  r  e  d  i  b  l  e
w  m  a  e  e  m  o  s  e  w  a  a  f  a  r
s  a  n  r  u  n  g  l  a  s  z  s  a  d  e
s  r  o  t  t  o  l  o  o  k  z  c  b  m  o
o  v  i  g  l  b  u  t  p  t  l  o  u  i  p
r  e  t  o  r  t  c  i  e  c  i  t  l  r  t
h  l  a  e  i  o  h  r  e  y  n  e  o  a  s
a  o  s  u  o  r  o  m  a  l  g  g  u  b  a
i  u  n  n  s  t  i  v  t  h  e  b  s  l  r
i  s  e  g  h  t  c  s  y  t  u  d  i  e  o
l  i  s  g  h  t  e  s  u  a  l  p  p  a  s
```

_____ _____ _____ _____ _____ _____ _____ _____

_____ _____ _____ _____ _____ _____

_____ _____ _____ _____ _____ _____ _____ _____

_____ _____ _____ _____ _____ _____ _____ _____ _____

_____ _____ _____ _____ _____!

Name _____

Let Out a Shriek!

Gravity Road was the first roller coaster in the United States. It was eighteen miles long and was built in Pennsylvania to carry coal from a mountain to the canal below.

Finish each sentence with a word about a roller coaster ride to complete the puzzle. Use the letters in *Gravity Road* as clues.

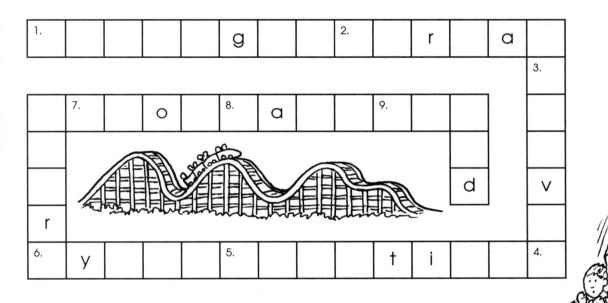

1. We formed a _____ line to wait to buy our tickets.

2. I let out a loud _____ at the end of the thrilling ride.

3. The _____ in the track made us all lean to the right.

4. The Flying Eagle is the most _____ ride!

5. We flew up and down in out seats during the _____ part of the ride.

6. The _____ was made of steel and was 6,000 feet long.

7. At the end of the ride, there was a long _____ straight down.

8. I cannot believe how _____ the roller coaster goes.

9. Sometimes the _____ is over 70 miles per hour.

Name _____

A Super Stretch

Who would not want to ride in a 100-foot limousine? This limousine was built in California, has 26 wheels, and is really incredible.

To find out what else this amazing limousine has, cross out the words that are not verbs in each box. Then, write the first letter of each word that can be a verb on the numbered blanks.

___ ___ ___ ___ ___ ___ ___ ___ ___ ___ ___ ___ ___
1   2   3   4   5   6   7   8   9   10 11 12 13

1. arrow ask camel	2. study stair desk	3. now glass watch	4. itch sooner wrist
5. county tomorrow mail	6. awful move strange	7. imagine above word	8. success nail excellent
9. enough rough grew	10. mile play company	11. open gentle course	
12. these grand operate	13. year laugh behind		

108

A Terrific Tongue

Did you know that a chameleon's tongue is often as long as its body? Its tongue shoots out so rapidly that a person can hardly see it!

Use this fascinating animal's name to complete each analogy.

1. Owl is to tree as king is to   c ☐ ☐ ☐ ☐ ☐ .

2. Eyes are to see as teeth are to   ☐ h ☐ .

3. Letters are to spell as numbers are to   a ☐ .

4. Inner is to inside as center is to   m ☐ ☐ ☐ ☐ ☐ .

5. Water is to ocean as sand is to   ☐ e ☐ ☐ ☐ ☐ .

6. Leg is to knee as arm is to   ☐ l ☐ ☐ ☐ .

7. Ending is to suffix as beginning is to   ☐ e ☐ ☐ ☐ ☐ .

8. One is to single as two is to   ☐ o ☐ ☐ ☐ ☐ .

9. Action is to verb as place is to   n ☐ ☐ ☐ .

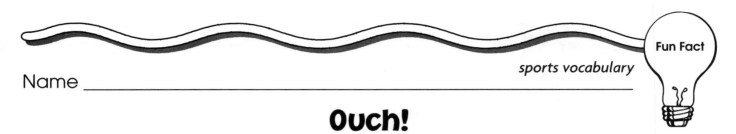

Ouch!

One professional baseball player was hit by a pitch 267 times. This is a major league record.

To find out this baseball player's name, write each baseball word in the puzzle. Then, use the number code to write the name on the blanks below.

Word Bank

bunt
catcher
diamond
error
foul
outfield
pitcher
player
rookie
strike
umpire

c h a m p i o n

___ ___ ___ ___ ___ ___ ___ ___ ___
1   2   3   4   5   6   7   8   9

Vocabulary Enrichment Activities

The following activities provide a fun and challenging way to help students expand their vocabularies. These activities can be used as individual or group activities. Vocabulary development will help improve students' reading, writing, and testing skills.

Call Out a Category

Write one of the following categories or one of your own on the chalkboard:
- three-syllable words
- words with double *l*s
- synonyms for good
- words that describe our city

Have the students brainstorm as many words as they can for each category.

Dynamic Dictionaries

Make mini-dictionaries for units in other subject areas such as science and social studies. Have the students write the meanings of the specialized vocabulary for each unit. Encourage the students to use their dictionaries as they read and study each unit.

Puzzle Power

Challenge students to make their own word games to share with each other. Use the grids on pages 112–114 as guides. Ideas for using the grids are as follows:

Crossword Puzzle Grid—Have students use their spelling lists to make crossword puzzles. After the words are written in the puzzles, students can use clean grids to shade in the boxes that are not to be used. Then the students can number the puzzles and write definitions on the appropriate lines at the bottom of the page.

Stair-Step Puzzle Grid—Have students write related 4- and 5-letter words in the shaded boxes of each puzzle. Next, have students complete the grids using the letters already written. Challenge them to write synonyms and antonyms for the words they use.

Word Search—Have students write the vocabulary words from specific subject areas in the grid. When all the words have been included, random letters can be added to fill the grids. List the words in the Word Bank. Exchange grids to solve.

Thesaurus Tunes

Have students write the words of their favorite songs or poems. Then, instruct the students to use a thesaurus to write synonyms for as many words in the songs or poems as possible. Finally, have each student read the new song or poem to the rest of the class.

Word of the Day

Have students keep a list of new words they encounter while reading. Use these words to help generate a "Word of the Day" list. Choose a word each day to spotlight. Have the students find the word's definition or definitions, phonetic spelling, and origin. If possible, the students can also brainstorm a list of synonyms and antonyms. Challenge the students to use the "Word of the Day" during the course of the day.

Crossword Puzzle Grid

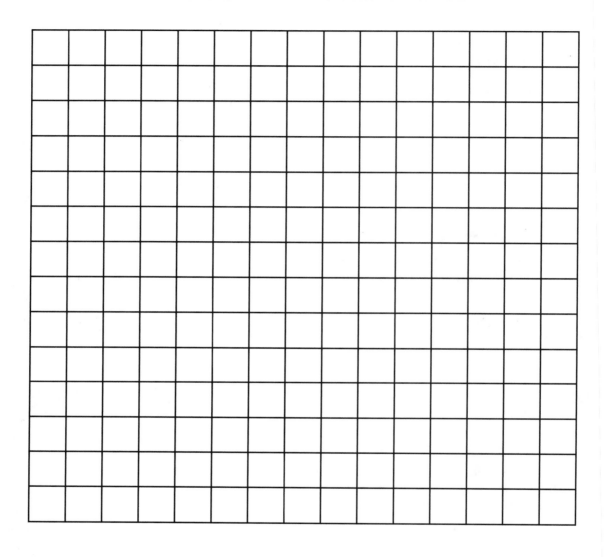

Across

_____
_____
_____
_____
_____
_____

Down

_____
_____
_____
_____
_____
_____

Stair-Step Puzzle Grid

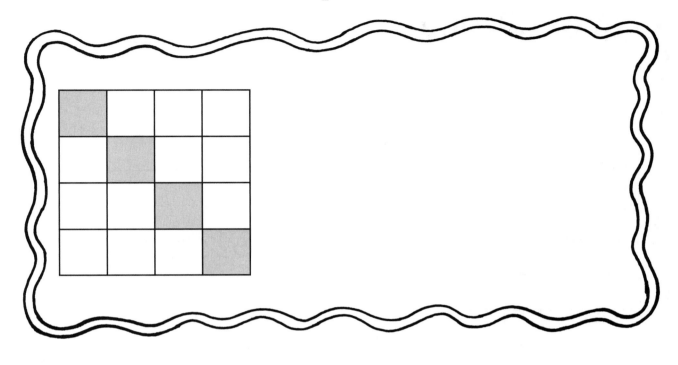

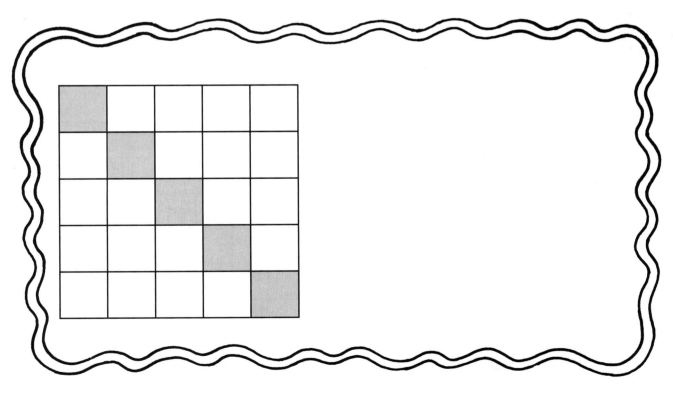

Name _____

Word Search Grid

Word Bank

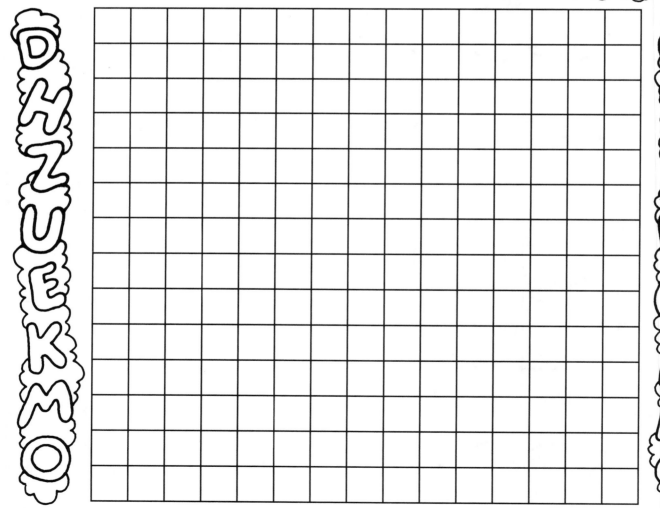

Vocabulary List

The following is a partial list of the vocabulary students will use while completing the word games in this book. The list was generated from third- and fourth-grade reading lists, as well as textbooks. Learning and understanding these words will help students achieve greater success in all academic areas.

absent	beach	choice	desert	explore	geese
accept	beef	citizen	discover	fabulous	general
accident	behind	claim	discrimination	fact	generous
addition	bicuspids	clear	disease	factory	gentle
admirable	bicycle	climate	distance	fail	geography
adventure	billion	coast	division	famous	germ
adverb	bleed	collar	double	favorite	glacier
agree	blind	college	download	fearless	glamorous
airtight	blizzard	compact disk	dream	federalist	globe
allow	bought	constitution	early	ferry	gosling
ambitious	brave	continent	education	finish	government
ambulance	breath	continue	elbow	firm	governor
anatomy	breeze	correct	elevator	flight	gram
ancestors	byte	cotton	eloquent	float	gravity
anger	cabinet	courageous	emergency	flock	greedy
applause	calcium	cradle	empty	flood	groom
artery	canines	crash	enamel	fluoride	group
astronomy	carbohydrates	crater	energy	foal	handmade
atlas	castle	creek	enough	forecast	handsome
atmosphere	cattle	crowd	enter	foreign	harbor
attic	cavity	crust	eraser	fort	harvest
author	celebrate	curtain	errand	fraction	haul
automobile	century	curve	error	frame	hazy
awesome	champion	damp	escape	free	height
backward	chapter	dangerous	even	freeze	helicopter
bait	cheap	dazzling	evening	fruits	herd
balcony	chef	debates	examination	fumble	heroic
basket	chew	decision	excited	galaxy	hibernate
batch	chief	dense	exercise	gallon	hidden
battle	chirp	dentin	experience	garage	history

honest	longest	parade	raw	stage	towel
horrible	mantle	paradise	reason	stalk	trade
hospital	marvelous	paraffin	receive	stare	tradition
hotel	mayor	paragraph	region	starve	trail
human	measure	parakeet	report	steamboat	travel
humid	medicine	paralegal	representative	steel	traveler
iceberg	memory	parallel	rest	stem	treasure
icicle	messenger	paralyze	reward	stethoscope	triangle
icy	meteorology	paramount	roots	straight	triathlon
ideas	meteors	parasol	route	student	tributary
igloo	meter	pebble	rule	study	triceps
immunization	midway	peek	saddle	submarine	trifocal
impolite	miles	perimeter	satellite	subtraction	trimester
important	millimeter	petal	score	sum	trilogy
inches	minerals	physician	seal	supply	triple
incisors	molars	piece	sealing	surgeon	triplet
incredible	monitor	piglet	search	surveyor	tripod
independence	moss	pioneer	seek	swallow	tunnel
infant	mountain	plague	segregation	sweep	umpire
intelligent	movement	plain	senator	sweet	uneven
Internet	multiplication	planet	sensational	system	unity
internist	narrow	plantation	shadow	tale	universe
iron	national	plateau	shovel	tame	vacation
judge	necessary	poison	sideline	tartar	valley
junior	noun	poult	sideways	taxi	vary
keep	nutrition	power	similar	temperature	vegetable
keyboard	ocean	precipitation	sleep	tepee	victory
knot	odd	prefix	sleet	terrible	village
laptop	orbit	president	sleeve	think	vitamins
lawyers	orthodontist	prize	slippery	thousand	volunteer
lazy	ounce	protein	smart	thread	watch
learn	owlet	proud	smooth	throw	watercolor
lecturer	owner	public	soar	thunderstorm	waterfall
length	pale	pulp	special	timid	weed
lever	pane	queen	specialist	tornado	wrap
liter	parachute	quiet	speed	tough	wrist

Page 4
Celebrate Work

Labor Day honors working people. It is celebrated on the first Monday in September throughout the United States, Puerto Rico, and Canada.

To find out what is important to every occupation, unscramble each occupation on the left. Use the pictures as clues. Then, write the letter from each box in order on the blanks below.

1. hcef — c h **e** f
2. tsdnelt — **d** e n t i s t
3. ruahot — a u **t** h o r
4. oenpmclai — p o l i **c** e m a n
5. atrchee — t e **a** c h e r
6. tasitr — a r t i s **t**
7. greethiriff — f **i** r e f i g h t e r
8. poilt — p i l **o** t
9. usner — **n** u r s e

E D U C A T I O N

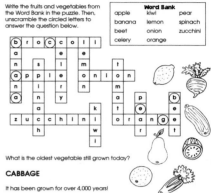

Page 5
Ice Cream Treat

In September of 1903, Italo Marchiony applied for a patent for the ice cream cone. Ice cream cones were served the following year at the 1904 World's Fair in St. Louis, Missouri.

Using the definition, write a five-letter word with the vowel sound listed on the ice cream. Then subtract one letter from the word to make a four-letter word with the same vowel sound. Continue until only the vowel is left.

short a sound
b a t c h
b a t h
b a t
a t
a

1. a group of cookies
2. a place to get clean
3. a small, flying animal
4. on or by

short u sound
s t u n g
n u t s
s u n
u s
u

1. to be pricked by a bee
2. hard-shelled dry fruits
3. a star that gives Earth heat
4. several people

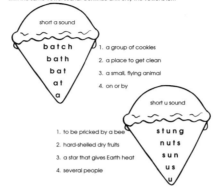

Page 6
Let's Eat Healthy!

To promote good eating habits, a week is spent in September to help encourage every person to eat five servings of fruits and vegetables every day. Fruits and vegetables provide our bodies with important vitamins and minerals.

Write the fruits and vegetables from the Word Bank in the puzzle. Then, unscramble the circled letters to answer the question below.

Word Bank
apple, banana, beet, celery, kiwi, lemon, onion, orange, pear, spinach, zucchini

(crossword with answers: broccoli, apple, onion, zucchini, orange, etc.)

What is the oldest vegetable still grown today?

CABBAGE

It has been grown for over 4,000 years!

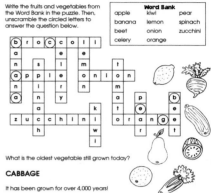

Page 7
A Giant Birthday

September 13 is Roald Dahl's birthday. This author has written many popular children's books including *Charlie and the Chocolate Factory*.

To find out the title of another book written by Roald Dahl, write a five-letter word with a long e sound for each definition. Then, write the shaded letters in order on the lines below to discover the title.

j	e	a	n	s
m	e	t	e	r
g	e	e	s	e
c	l	e	a	n
d	r	e	a	m
t	e	e	t	h
s	w	e	e	t
a	g	r	e	e
i	d	e	a	s
q	u	e	e	n
t	e	p	e	e
l	e	a	v	e
b	e	a	c	h

1. denim pants
2. metric linear measurement
3. more than one goose
4. not dirty
5. a thought while sleeping
6. used for chewing
7. a taste with lots of sugar
8. to go along with another's idea
9. thoughts
10. a female ruler
11. one type of Native American home
12. to exit
13. a sandy shore

JAMES AND THE GIANT PEACH

Page 8
Follow the Path

On September 16, 1602, the Mayflower left Plymouth, England, for America. This ship carried 102 passengers across the Atlantic Ocean.

To sail the ship below, write the word for each definition. The last letter of each word is the first letter for the next word.

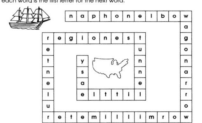

(path puzzle: nap, phone, elbow, weak, narrow, regions, nest, etc.)

1. a short rest
2. a device used to call someone
3. the joint in the middle of an arm
4. a wheeled cart
5. not very wide
6. a long, thin animal with no legs or backbone
7. a small metric measurement
8. a law
9. to go into a building
10. an area of a country
11. a place a bird may live
12. a covered passage
13. very small
14. simple

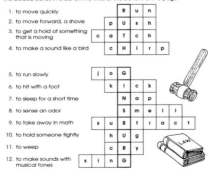

Page 9
Almost the Same

The autumnal equinox is one of two days during the year when the sun is directly above the equator. On these two days, day and night are nearly the same length everywhere on Earth.

Night and *knight* are homophones because they sound the same but are spelled differently. Circle the homophone in the puzzle for each word in the Word Bank. Words will go across, up, down, and diagonally.

Word Bank
dear, fairy, hall, heard, made, no, not, pail, pain, peace, pour, reed, some, sore, sun, wood

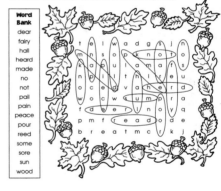

Page 10
Stamp and Mail

The first United States Postmaster General was appointed in September of 1789. At that time there were only 75 post offices. Today, almost 570 million pieces of mail are delivered daily.

Use the definitions and the letters in *stamp* and *mail* to complete each puzzle.

s	m	a	r	t
s	t	a	g	e
t	r	a	s	h
f	r	a	m	e
s	w	e	e	p

1. very clever
2. a platform
3. garbage
4. a picture border
5. to clean a floor

m	e	l	t
f	a	c	t
s	w	i	m
r	e	a	l

6. turn into liquid
7. statement that is true
8. move in water
9. not fake

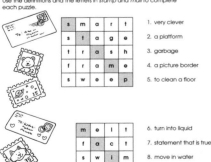

Page 11
Female Justices

On September 25, 1981, Sandra Day O'Connor became the first female justice of the United States Supreme Court. Twelve years later, another woman was appointed to this court.

To find out the name of the second female Supreme Court Justice, write a verb in the boxes for each definition. To spell her name, write the letters from the bolded boxes in order on the lines at the bottom of the page.

1. to move quickly — **R** u n
2. to move forward, a shove — p **U** s h
3. to get a hold of something that is moving — c a **T** c h
4. to make a sound like a bird — c **H** i r p

5. to run slowly — j o **g**
6. to hit with a foot — k **i** c k
7. to sleep for a short time — **N** a p
8. to sense an odor — s m e **l** l
9. to take away in math — s u **B** t r a c t
10. to hold someone tightly — h **U** g
11. to weep — c **R** y
12. to make sounds with musical tones — s i n **g**

Ruth _____ Bader _____ Ginsburg

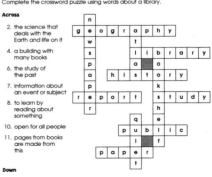

Page 12
Get Your Card Here!

September is library card sign-up month. In the United States, there are 15,000 public libraries. One of the first public libraries in the United States was started in 1833 in Peterborough, New Hampshire.

Complete the crossword puzzle using words about a library.

Across
2. the science that deals with the Earth and life on it
4. a building with many books
6. the study of the past
7. information about an event or subject
8. to learn by reading about something
10. open for all people
11. pages from books are made from this

Down
1. a daily or weekly publication
3. a book of maps
5. a ledge to place books
9. making little noise

(crossword answers: geography, library, history, report, study, public, paper, etc.)

Page 13
It's a Home Run!

On October 1, 1961, Roger Maris, a New York Yankee, hit his 61st home run of the season to break Babe Ruth's home run record. Another record-breaking home-run slugger celebrates his birthday on this day.

To find out who he is, complete the puzzle. Unscramble each word on the left. Each word includes the letters B, A, and T. Use the pictures as clues. Then write the letter from each box in order on the lines below to learn the home run slugger's name.

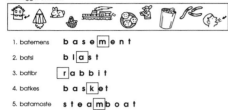

1. batemens — b a s e **m** e n t
2. batsl — b l **a** s t
3. batlbr — **r** a b b i t
4. batkes — b a s **k** e t
5. batamoste — s t e a **m** b o a t
6. bathc — b a t **c** h
7. batngti — b a t t i n **g**
8. basteektsaw — **w** a s t e b a s k e t
9. bati — b a **i** t
10. bathre — b **r** **e** a t h

MARK McGWIRE

Page 14
Sweet Treats

What is your favorite dessert? Double your pleasure with two desserts in October to celebrate National Dessert Month.

Double your fun by completing the crossword puzzle with words containing double letters. Use the clues from each sentence to help you.

Across
1. The teacher gave me a cookie because all my answers were _____.
5. I won a treat when I shot the _____ in the center of the target.
6. The small _____ I found by the river reminded me of a jelly bean.
8. We walked across the _____ ice to get some hot chocolate.
9. The ice cream truck was too wide for the _____ tunnel.
10. The car was completely covered with snow because of the _____.

Down
1. The mouse nibbled on the _____.
2. The _____ hopped through the garden looking for a carrot.
3. We need to _____ the street to get to the bakery.
4. I want to _____ every bite of that chocolate cake.
7. Mom ran an _____ to buy a sweet surprise.

Crossword answers:
- c o r r e c t — c s
- h a — a r r o w
- p e b b l e e — r s
- e b — r s l
- s l i p p e r y s — l
- e t — a o
- n a r r o w
- b l i z z a r d

Page 15
Across the Atlantic

On October 12, 1492, after traveling across the Atlantic Ocean from Spain, Christopher Columbus landed on an island in the West Indies.

To find out what Columbus named the island, solve the puzzle. Use each clue to write a word about Columbus' expedition. The first letter for each word has been given. Then write the circled letters in order on the blanks below to learn the island's name.

1. the land next to the sea
2. a person who works on a boat
3. a large body of salt water
4. a measurement used to tell the distance between two cities
5. a person who travels
6. an exciting experience
7. to declare one's own
8. to give one thing in return for something else
9. a course used for traveling
10. to investigate a new place

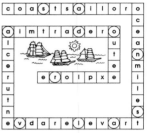

Puzzle:
- c o a s t s a i l o r o
- a i m t r a d e r o
- l — u
- r e r o l p x e t
- u — n
- n — s
- e v d a r e l e v a r t

SAN SALVADOR

Page 16
Rain Forest Adventure

A week is spent in mid-October to raise awareness of the world's rain forests. Rain forests are home to half of the world's plant and animal species.

Take a journey into a rain forest. Use the code to fill in the letters of each missing word.

A B C D E F G H I K L M N O P R S T U V

To celebrate World Rain Forest Week, you are about to take an imaginary journey through a rain forest. As you step onto the **d a m p** forest floor, you immediately hear **i n s e c t s** buzzing and **b i r d s** screeching. A toad hops across the forest's carpet which is made of **m o s s**, leaves, and branches. Growing from the **t r u n k** of a tree is a beautiful **o r c h i d**. You continue to walk through the **d e n s e** forest. The **t e m p e r a t u r e** is comfortable, but the air

Page 17

is **h u m i d**. Soon it begins to rain. You find shelter under the huge leaves of a tree. A monkey climbs a nearby **s t a l k** for the **b a n a n a s** at the top. An emerald tree **b o a** with yellow stripes slithers from tree to tree.

When the rain stops, you continue your journey. You see several cacao trees in the **d i s t a n c e**. Pods grow on these trees. Inside the pods are beans. **C h o c o l a t e** comes from the beans. As night falls, you spy a jaguar running near a river.

Your day has included many **i n c r e d i b l e** sights and sounds of the jungle world. As you fall asleep, you dream about tomorrow's adventure.

Page 18
Look It Up

October 16 is Dictionary Day. This special day celebrates the birthday of the American who published a small school dictionary in 1806.

To find out this American's name, complete the puzzle. Write a two-syllable word for each definition. Then, write the shaded letters in order on the blanks below to spell the name.

f	i	n	g	e	r
d	o	l	l	a	r
a	b	s	e	n	t
h	i	d	d	e	n
w	i	n	d	o	w
s	e	c	r	e	t
b	a	t	t	l	e
c	i	r	c	u	s
w	r	i	t	e	r
s	u	m	m	e	r
r	e	c	e	s	s

1. slender part attached to a hand
2. paper money unit
3. not present
4. to be kept out of sight
5. an opening in a wall
6. known only to oneself
7. a long struggle or combat
8. where clowns perform
9. a person who writes
10. the season after spring
11. a break time during school

NOAH WEBSTER

Page 19
Rhyme Time

Black Poetry Day is celebrated in mid-October. Alice Walker and Gwendolyn Brooks are two popular African-American poets.

To find out the name of another popular African-American poet, think of two words that rhyme for each definition. For example, a noisy mob would be a loud crowd. Then, use the number code to spell the poet's name on the blanks below.

1. a comical rabbit — f u n n y   b u n n y
2. an amusing town — w i t t y   c i t y
3. a solid bacteria — f i r m   g e r m
4. an outstanding ice shoe — g r e a t   s k a t e
5. pleasant rodents — n i c e   m i c e
6. a nutty flower — c r a z y   d a i s y
7. a pretty salamander — c u t e   n e w t
8. a five-cent cucumber — n i c k l e   p i c k l e
9. a fake horse — p h o n y   p o n y
10. a happy evergreen shrub — j o l l y   h o l l y
11. to take a dinner — s t e a l   m e a l

LANGSTON HUGHES

Page 20
Pizza Party

October is National Pizza Month. Raffaele Esposito, an Italian baker, invented pizza Margherita in 1889. He created a pie with the same colors as the Italian flag.

Use the pictures and the letters in *dough* and *cheese* as clues to complete each puzzle.

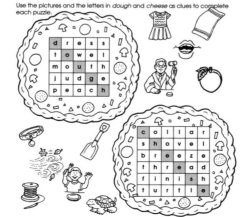

First pizza:
- d r e s s
- t o w e l
- m o u t h
- j u d g e
- p e a c h

Second pizza:
- c o l l a r
- s h o v e l
- b r e e z e
- t h r e a d
- f i n i s h
- t u r t l e

Page 21
Computer Chatter

October is Computer Learning Month. One of the first computers was built in the early 1940s by Howard Aiken. It was called the Mark I and used 530 miles of wire.

Find each computer word from the Word Bank in the puzzle. The words will go forward, backward, up, down, and diagonally. Then, starting with the first uncircled letter, write every other uncircled letter on the blanks below to answer the riddle.

Word Bank
byte
compact disk
download
Internet
keyboard
laptop
memory
monitor
mouse
printer
scanner
software
virus

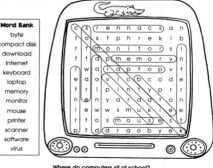

Where do computers sit at school?

AT THEIR FLOPPY DESKS!

Word Games: Grades 3–4

Page 22
An Incredible Feast

Halloween has been celebrated in many countries for centuries. For many years, it included a feast for those who led good lives.

Follow each word from the Word Bank through the maze to get the bats to the candy. The words will go across, up, and down.

Word Bank

costumes	eerie	gloomy
haunted	jack-o-lantern	monster
mummy	October	pumpkin
skeleton	spider	

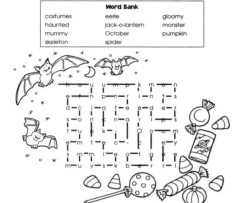

Page 23
Bony Banter

Write the Halloween word for each definition. The bolded boxes will answer the riddle below.

1. parts of a skeleton — b o n e s
2. a disguise — m a s k
3. causing a feeling of fear; rhymes with sleepy — c r e e p y
4. a very dark color — b l a c k
5. what you get at Halloween — t r e a t s
6. the sound an owl makes — h o o t
7. a small furry flying animal — b a t
8. Earth's satellite — m o o n

Why did the skeleton sit outside?

To get a **SKELETAN** !

Page 24
Today's Forecast

On November 1, 1870, the United States Weather Bureau made its first weather observations. Today, weather satellites orbit Earth continuously to gather information about the weather.

Use the Word Bank to write the weather word for each definition on pages 24 and 25. Then, use the number code to fill in the boxes below the definitions to discover three more weather words.

Word Bank

barometer	blizzard	flood	foggy
forecast	humidity	hurricane	lightning
measure	satellite	sleet	spring
sprinkle	thunder	tornado	weather

1. freezing rain — s l e e t
2. full of low clouds — f o g g y
3. to cover with water — f l o o d
4. a funnel of wind — t o r n a d o
5. to find the amount — m e a s u r e

m e t e o r o l o g y

Page 25

6. the condition of the air — w e a t h e r
7. to predict the weather — f o r e c a s t
8. a loud, rumbling sound — t h u n d e r
9. the season before summer — s p r i n g
10. to rain gently — s p r i n k l e
11. a flash of light caused by electricity moving between clouds — l i g h t n i n g

p r e c i p i t a t i o n

12. a spacecraft used to forecast the weather — s a t e l l i t e
13. a storm with strong winds — h u r r i c a n e
14. a heavy snowstorm — b l i z z a r d
15. water vapor in the air — h u m i d i t y
16. an instrument used to measure the pressure of the atmosphere — b a r o m e t e r

t h e r m o m e t e r

Page 26
Take a Ride

There are many ways we get from one place to another. On November 5, 1895, George Seldon of Rochester, New York, received the first patent for this very important type of transportation.

To find out what the patent was for, complete the crossword puzzle. Then, unscramble the shaded letters on the blanks below.

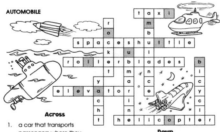

Across

1. a car that transports passengers where they want to go
4. a spacecraft that returns to land on Earth
6. in-line skates
9. a small room that can be raised or lowered
10. an aircraft with blades above it

Down

2. transports sick people
3. a spacecraft driven through the air by a stream of hot gasses
5. a ship that travels under water
7. a vehicle with two wheels
8. a large, luxury boat

Page 27
A Slam Dunk

James Naismith, the inventor of basketball, was born on November 6, 1861. *Incredible* and *unbelievable* are two synonyms which describe basketball players.

One of these incredible basketball players is Michael Jordan. Use the letters from his name and the synonym clues to complete the puzzle. Then, use the number code to complete part of a quote by this unbelievable athlete.

M

I t — thing
C a p — hat
H u n t — search
A t t i c — upstairs
E s c a p e — flee
L a w y e r s — attorneys
J u n i o r — younger
O w n e r — possessor
R i c h — wealthy
D o g — mutt
A t — there

N

"I can accept failure...
But **I can't accept not trying.**"

Page 28
A Purr-fect Pet

Cat Week begins on the first Sunday in November. Wildcats were first tamed about 5,000 years ago. Some people had pet cats 4,000 years ago.

To find out who these people were, write a word for each definition. Each word has the letters C, A, and T in it. The letter C has been given for each word as a clue. The bolded boxes will tell you the answer.

1. c e l e b r a t e
2. a c t i n g
3. f a c t o r y
4. c h a p t e r
5. v a c a t i o n
6. c l i m a t e
7. c u r t a i n
8. c a b i n e t
9. c o a s t

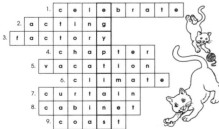

1. to honor a special event
2. pretending
3. a building where things are made
4. a section of a book
5. a period of rest from school
6. the weather conditions in a place
7. a covering for a window
8. a piece of furniture with shelves and doors
9. the land next to the sea

Page 29
And the Winner Is...

Election Day is held the first Tuesday after the first Monday in November. National elections throughout the United States are held on this day.

Find a path for the ballot to reach the ballot box. Follow the letters of the words about elections from the Word Bank forward, backward, up, down, and diagonally.

Word Bank

citizen	constitution
experience	government
governor	mayor
president	national
senator	representative

Page 30
A Cold Trip South

Captain Nathanial Palmer is believed to have discovered Antarctica on November 18, 1820. The South Pole is located there. Another American made many expeditions in the early 1900s to this unpopulated continent.

To find out his name, unscramble the following words with the *ar* sound. Use the sentences as clues. Then, write the shaded letters in order on the blanks below.

1. A R T P — p a r t — I like that _____ of the story.
2. A R L S I I M — s i m i l a r — Brown and tan are _____ colors.
3. A R Y C R — c a r r y — I will _____ the flag.
4. A R V T E S H — h a r v e s t — It is time to _____ the corn.
5. A R H E S — s h a r e — Please _____ the cookies with her.
6. A R F S C — s c a r f — I wore a _____ because it was cold.
7. A R G N E D — g a r d e n — The flowers in the _____ are blooming.
8. A R O R H B — h a r b o r — The boat sailed away from the _____.
9. A R Y R M — m a r r y — My aunt is going to _____ her boyfriend.
10. A R G E A G — g a r a g e — My dad put the car in the _____.
11. A R C D S E — s c a r e d — The loud noise _____ me.

RICHARD BYRD

Page 31
A Memorable Speech

On November 19, 1863, President Abraham Lincoln delivered the *Gettysburg Address*. This famous Civil War speech began "Four score and seven years ago . . .".

To find out in which state this speech was delivered, complete the puzzle. Finish each double consonant word. Use the definitions as clues. Then unscramble the boxed letters on the blanks below.

s u p p l y	1. to provide something needed
p e p p e r	2. a spice often used with salt
s l o p p y	3. very messy
s l i p p e r	4. a light shoe easy to put on the foot
g a l l o n	5. a measurement unit for liquids
v a l l e y	6. low land between hills or mountains
v i l l a g e	7. a small town
c o l l e g e	8. a school after high school
b a t t l e	9. a fight during a war
c o t t o n	10. a type of cloth
b u t t o n	11. used to fasten a shirt
r o t t e n	12. spoiled

PENNSYLVANIA

Page 32
Native American Tribes

When the pilgrims arrived, there were many different Native American tribes living in North America. Each tribe's way of life was dependent on the area of the country in which the tribe lived.

Circle the names of the Native American tribes listed below. The names will go forward, backward, up, down, and diagonally.

Anasazi   Apache   Cherokee
Cheyenne   Choctaw   Iroquois
Navajo   Seminole   Seneca
Shawnee   Shoshoni
Sioux   Ute

Page 33
A Day to Feast

Thanksgiving is celebrated on the fourth Thursday in November. It is the oldest American holiday.

Thanksgiving is a compound word. Use the picture clues to write more compound words on the lines. Then, use the number code to answer the Thanksgiving riddle below.

1. h o r s e f l y
2. h o m e s i c k
3. e y e g l a s s e s
4. t o o t h p a s t e
5. s u r f b o a r d
6. b u t t e r f l y
7. c l a s s r o o m
8. s u n s h i n e
9. f r o s t b i t e

Why is a couch like a turkey?

BECAUSE THEY'RE BOTH FULL OF STUFFING!

Page 34
Festival of Lights

Hanukkah is a Jewish holiday also known as the Festival of Lights. It is celebrated for eight days. A candle is lit each night during this celebration.

Use the sentence and synonym clues below to fill in each set of boxes. Then, write each letter from the bolded boxes in order in the last set of boxes to learn the name of the special Jewish candle holder.

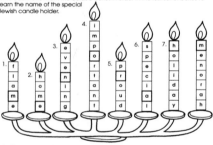

1. The _____ of the candle is orange. (fire)
2. The family celebrates in their _____. (habitat)
3. In the _____, they light the candle. (night)
4. Hanukkah is an _____ Jewish holiday. (significant)
5. Ian is _____ of his family. (pleased)
6. Each night the family opens a _____ gift. (outstanding)
7. Rachel was excited for the _____ season. (vacation)

Page 35
Fill It Up

On December 1, 1913, the first gas station was opened in Pittsburgh, Pennsylvania.

To find out how much gas was sold the first day, complete the puzzle using the math and measurement clues. Then, read the first letter of each word to learn the amount.

t h o u s a n d	1. 10 times 100
h e i g h t	2. the distance from top to bottom
i n c h e s	3. the 12 parts of a foot
r u l e r	4. a 12-inch straight edge used to measure objects
t h i r d	5. between second and fourth
y a r d	6. a measurement equal to three feet
g r a m	7. a metric unit of weight less than an ounce
a d d i t i o n	8. the adding of numbers
l e n g t h	9. the distance from one end to the other
l i t e r	10. a metric unit similar to a quart
o u n c e	11. a small unit of weight
n i n e t y	12. 10 less than 100
s e c o n d s	13. the 60 parts of a minute

Page 36
Deep Freeze

Clarence Birdseye was the founder of the frozen-foods industry. He was born on December 9, 1886, in Brooklyn, New York.

Complete each analogy. The shaded boxes will spell three frozen food products.

p	o	l	e
w	e	s	t
n	e	a	t
t	o	e	s

1. Shovel is to digging as _____ is to fishing.
2. North is to south as east is to _____.
3. Long is to short as _____ is to messy.
4. Fingers are to hand as _____ are to foot.

5. Warm is to hot as cool is to _____.
6. Worker is to _____ as player is to coach.
7. Boats are to river as _____ are to road.
8. High is to low as up is to _____.

c	o	l	d
b	o	s	s
c	a	r	s
d	o	w	n

f	a	c	t
c	i	t	y
l	o	s	e
d	i	s	h

9. Real is to fantasy as _____ is to opinion.
10. County is to state as suburb is to _____.
11. Satisfied is to win as disappointed is to _____.
12. Cup is to drink as _____ is to eat.

Page 37
A Long Journey

On December 13, 1577, Sir Francis Drake set sail from Plymouth, England. It took him three years to sail around the world.

Finish each sentence in the center of the puzzle with a three-syllable word from the Word Bank. Write each word in the puzzle around the world. Be careful; not all the words from the Word Bank will be used. The shaded letters will spell the name of Sir Francis Drake's ship.

GOLDEN HIND

Word Bank

adventure	Atlantic	century	continue
dangerous	decision	discover	estimate
history	messenger	Pacific	pioneer

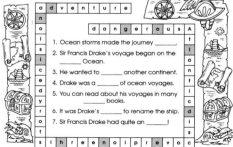

1. Ocean storms made the journey _____.
2. Sir Francis Drake's voyage began on the _____ Ocean.
3. He wanted to _____ another continent.
4. Drake had a _____ of ocean voyages.
5. You can read about his voyages in many _____ books.
6. It was Drake's _____ to rename the ship.
7. Sir Francis Drake had quite an _____.

Page 38
Flying High

On December 17, 1903, Orville and Wilbur Wright completed the first airplane flight near Kitty Hawk, North Carolina.

To find out how long the first flight lasted, complete the puzzle. In each set of boxes, write the homophone for the missing word in each sentence. The bolded boxes will tell how long this flight was.

s t a r e	1. Beth climbed every _____ to the top of the building.
w a i t	2. His _____ has changed to 70 pounds.
s t e a l	3. The bridge was made of _____.
s e a l i n g	4. The man was so tall that he bumped his head on the _____.
v a r y	5. John is a _____ good skater.
g r e a t	6. Mom will _____ the cheese for the pizza.
s e w	7. I need to _____ the seeds before it rains.
s e e	8. We sailed across the _____.
c l o s e	9. Your clean _____ are in the laundry basket.
b o a r d	10. Rayna was _____ because there was nothing to do.
n i g h t	11. The _____ rode his horse to the castle.
m a d e	12. We need a _____ to clean your messy room.
s o a r	13. My feet were _____ from walking all day.

Page 39
Read the Clue

On December 21, 1913, the first crossword puzzle appeared in the *New York World* newspaper. This type of word puzzle is still popular today.

Complete the crossword puzzle with a word containing a silent letter.

Across

1. behaving badly
4. powerful
6. to be very hungry
7. to cover a package
8. a long reptile with no legs
9. a legend
10. from another country

Down

1. a sound
2. what a clock measures
3. good-looking
5. awful, terrible

n a u g h t y
m i g h t y
s t a r v e
w r a p
s n a k e
t a l e
f o r e i g n

Page 40
Cold and Hot

The shortest day of each year in the northern hemisphere occurs on December 21 or 22. This date marks the beginning of winter. At this same time, the southern hemisphere is having the opposite season (summer).

Write the antonym for each clue. Then, unscramble the circled letters on the lines below to spell a winter word.

on	1. off
old	2. young
most	3. least
float	4. sink
simple	5. difficult
black	6. white
past	7. future
few	8. lots
in	9. out

SNOWFLAKE

Page 41
A Jolly Season

Christmas is celebrated all over the world on December 25. There are many customs and traditions associated with this Christian holiday.

One custom is to decorate an evergreen tree. Use each letter in the tree lights and each one-word clue to write 10 Christmas words.

1. ornament
2. reindeer
3. presents
4. caroling
5. church
6. stockings
7. chimney
8. sleigh
9. wreath
10. peace

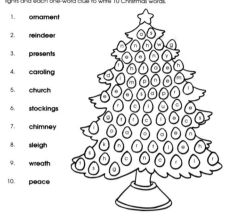

Page 42
Kwanzaa Celebration

Kwanzaa is a seven-day holiday that lasts from December 26 until January 1. It celebrates African cultures and the lives of African Americans. The name *Kwanzaa* comes from Swahili words which mean "first fruits."

Circle the important Kwanzaa celebration words listed below. The words will go forward, backward, up, down, and diagonally. Then, write the remaining letters in order on the blanks below to spell the Swahili words from which the name *Kwanzaa* comes.

ancestors
art
black
candles
culture
dance
faith
family
feast
fun
gifts
green
harvest
honor
music
purpose
tradition
unity
red

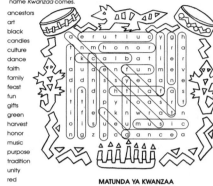

MATUNDA YA KWANZAA

Page 43
A Sweet-Smelling Parade

Everyone loves a parade! The Tournament of Roses Parade is held on New Year's Day in Pasadena, California. The founders of this parade wanted to celebrate California's warm weather. The opposite kind of weather, cold and snowy, was happening in much of the rest of the country.

Write the antonym of each clue. The last letter of each word will be the first letter of the next word. Then, unscramble the letters from the shaded boxes to find out what is used to make the floats in this parade. Write the answer on the blanks below.

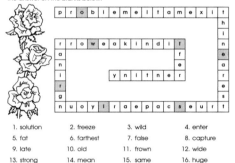

1. solution	2. freeze	3. wild	4. enter
5. fat	6. farthest	7. false	8. capture
9. late	10. old	11. frown	12. wide
13. strong	14. mean	15. same	16. huge

FLOWERS

Page 44
A Super System

Louis Braille was born on January 4, 1809, near Paris, France. He developed a system of reading called Braille.

To learn more about this remarkable man and this reading system, use the system to complete the passage.

a	b	c	d	e	f	g	h	i	j	k	l	m

n	o	p	q	r	s	t	u	v	w	x	y	z

In 1824, 15-year-old **Louis Braille**

developed this **system** to help

teach blind children to read

and write. It consists of **raised dots** for each letter

of the alphabet and can be read by **touch** .

Louis Braille became blind after an **accident** when he

was only **three** years old.

Page 45
Count the Votes

On January 7, 1789, the first presidential election was held in the United States. George Washington was elected. The person who finished second became the vice president.

To find out his name, unscramble the names of the states which participated in the first election. Then, write the circled letters in order to spell the name of the vice president.

1. wne seejyr — New Jersey
2. stasmetshcuas — Massachusetts
3. cuttinenoc — Connecticut
4. raivinig — Virginia
5. senplnavyain — Pennsylvania
6. nwe phraemhis — New Hampshire
7. wlearead — Delaware
8. raigoeg — Georgia
9. dlarmyan — Maryland
10. thuos raonialc — South Carolina

Vice President **JOHN ADAMS**

Page 46
A Historic Flight

On January 11, 1935, Amelia Earhart became the first woman to fly solo across the Pacific Ocean, from Hawaii to California.

To find out where she began this 18-hour flight, complete the puzzle. Write the word in the puzzle from the Word Bank that completes each sentence about Amelia Earhart. Then, write the letters from the shaded boxes in order on the blanks below to learn the city where this historic flight began.

1. hospital
2. pilot
3. Kansas
4. woman
5. goggles
6. public
7. flight
8. bought

Word Bank
bought
flight
goggles
hospital
Kansas
pilot
public
woman

1. Amelia Earhart was once a volunteer at a _____.
2. After riding in an airplane, she wanted to become a _____.
3. She was born in 1897 in the state of _____.
4. She was the first _____ to fly solo across the Atlantic Ocean.
5. She wore a helmet and _____ when she flew.
6. She often checked out books at the _____ library.
7. Her solo _____ across the Atlantic took 15 hours.
8. When she was 25, she _____ her first airplane.

The flight began in **HONOLULU** .

Page 47
The Freedom Doctor

Martin Luther King, Jr. was born on January 15, 1929. Dr. King's birthday became a national holiday in 1983 and is celebrated on the third Monday in January.

Write the word from the Word Bank in the puzzle for each definition. Not all the words will be used. Then, write the letters from the bolded boxes in order on the blanks below to learn the name of the famous speech given by

Word Bank
author
boycott
civil rights
discrimination
eloquent
equality
justice
intelligent
leader
minister
movement
nonviolent
protesters
segregation

intelligent
civil rights
author
nonviolent
eloquent
equality
discrimination
minister
justice
segregation
movement

1. very smart and wise
2. the qualities of personal liberties
3. a person who writes a book
4. not forceful
5. using words well
6. the condition of being equal
7. an unfair difference in treatment
8. a person who conducts a church service
9. fair treatment
10. the practice of setting one racial group apart from another
11. the actions of a group to reach some goal

The name of the speech is " **I HAVE A DREAM.**"

Page 48
Doctor Blackwell

The first woman in the United States to receive a medical degree was Elizabeth Blackwell. On January 23, 1849, in Geneva, New York, Elizabeth became Dr. Blackwell.

Write each medical word in the puzzle. Start with the word with the most letters.

Word Bank
anatomy
artery
disease
emergency
examination
immunization
internist
medicine
physician
specialist
stethoscope
surgeon

stethoscope
medicine
artery
internist
anatomy
emergency
disease

Page 49
Strike It Rich

James Marshall discovered gold in California on January 24, 1848. For the next two years, thousands rushed to California in search of gold. They were nicknamed "forty-niners."

Use the clues to complete the puzzles with the words forty and niners.

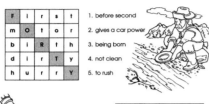

F	I	r	s	t
m	O	T	o	r
b	I	R	T	h
d	I	r	t	Y
h	u	r	r	Y

1. before second
2. gives a car power
3. being born
4. not clean
5. to rush

6. not wide
7. it shows a reflection
8. one who dances
9. a part of speech
10. to tell about something
11. large animals with manes

N	a	r	r	o	w
m	I	r	r	o	r
d	a	N	c	e	r
a	d	v	E	r	b
r	e	p	o	R	t
h	o	r	s	e	s

Page 50
Name That Tune

National Kazoo Day is celebrated in late January. By humming into this instrument, you can play any song you want.

Complete the puzzle using the clues to the right. Each word will contain oo in it.

moo	1. cow sound
wool	2. sheep hair
roots	3. flower parts
snooze	4. short sleep
shampoo	5. hair wash
scooter	6. sidewalk vehicle
smooth	7. not rough
tooth	8. chewing tool
wood	9. part of tree used to build things
zoo	10. place for animals

Page 51
Double Play

On January 29, 1936, the Baseball Hall of Fame was established. It opened in Cooperstown, New York, in 1939. Walter Johnson, Christy Mathewson, and Honus Wagner were three of the first five members.

To find out the names of the other two players, find a single word for each group that makes three compound words. Then, use the number code to write the players' names on the lines on page 52.

1. waterfall / watercolor / watermelon
2. outfield / outfit / outside
3. raincoat / rainbow / rainfall
4. airplane / airmail / airtight
5. sidewalk / sideline / sideways
6. footprint / footstep / football
7. strawberry / blueberry / gooseberry
8. sailboat / houseboat / motorboat

Page 52

9. someday / sometime / someday
10. sunshine / sunflower / sunglasses
11. handcuff / handwriting / handmade
12. campfire / campground / campsite

TY COBB and **BABE RUTH**

Page 53
Incredible Americans

February is African-American History Month. In 1926, Carter G. Woodson started this month-long tribute as a time to learn about many important African-Americans.

Follow each name of an important African-American from the Name Bank through the maze. The names will go forward, backward, up, and down.

Name Bank

Maya Angelou	Louis Armstrong	George Washington Carver
Jackie Joyner-Kersee	Thurgood Marshall	
Jesse Owens	Rosa Parks	Sidney Poitier
Colin Powell	Jackie Robinson	Wilma Rudolph
Clarence Thomas	Harriet Tubman	Carter G. Woodson

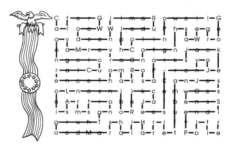

Page 54
Brush and Floss

National Children's Dental Health Week begins the first Sunday in February.

Find each word about dental health from the Word Bank in the puzzle. The words will go up, down, forward, backward, and diagonally. Then, to learn a fact about teeth, write the letters remaining in order on the blanks below.

Word Bank

bicuspids	bite	calcium	canines
cavity	dentin	dentist	enamel
fluoride	gum	incisors	molars
plaque	pulp	orthodontist	
root	tartar	toothbrush	

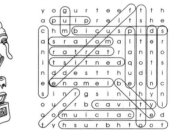

YOUR TEETH ARE THE HARDEST THINGS IN YOUR BODY!

Page 55
Is Spring Here?

Groundhog Day is celebrated on February 2. The pilgrims brought this tradition to America from England.

Write a word for each definition. Then, use the number code to discover two words about this special day. To learn about this tradition, fill in the missing words in the passage below with words from the activity.

1. the second month of the year — **February**
2. a dark area made by blocked light — **shadow**
3. an opening — **hole**
4. a custom that is passed along — **tradition**
5. opposite of front — **back**
6. giving light — **shining**
7. the season after winter — **spring**
8. a day without sun — **cloudy**
9. a place where wild animals sleep — **den**

| w | o | o | d | c | h | u | c | k |

| h | i | b | e | r | n | a | t | e |

The groundhog, or **woodchuck**, is a large rodent. The American **tradition** says that on the morning of **February** 2, the groundhog comes out of its **hole** and looks around. If the sun is **shining** and the groundhog sees its **shadow**, it will be scared **back** into its **den** and will **hibernate** for six more weeks. If the day is **cloudy**, the groundhog will stay out, and **spring** will arrive soon.

Page 56
Earn Some Cash

The first paper money in America was issued on February 3, 1690, in Massachusetts. It was used to pay soldiers.

Use each letter group from the Letter Bank to make a five-letter word on each piece of paper money. Use each letter group only once.

Letter Bank

tr	ave	~~sc~~	oup	cr
ten	pow	sc	er	ize
~~mon~~	gr	~~per~~	ade	~~th~~
ore	pr	owd	th	br

pa per
mon ey
pow er
tr ade
sc ore
cr owd
gr oup
br ave
pr ize
ten th

Page 57
Time for School

The first public school in America was started on February 13, 1635, in Boston, Massachusetts. It was called the Boston Latin School.

Starting at the bottom of each puzzle, fill in the boxes with words about school from the Word Bank. The last letter of each word is the first letter of the next word.

Word Bank

desk
help
kindergarten
know
listen
math
paper
read
recess
school
teacher
test
think
write

Page 58
Around and Around

George Washington Gale Ferris was born on February 14, 1859, in Galesburg, Illinois. He invented the Ferris wheel to celebrate the 400th anniversary of Christopher Columbus' discovery of the New World.

Write a word in each seat of the Ferris wheel using the words with an *ee* from the Word Bank and the definitions below. Not all of the words will be used.

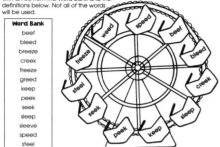

Word Bank

beef
bleed
breeze
creek
freeze
greed
keep
peek
seek
sleep
sleeve
speed
steel
weed

1. quick
2. meat from a cow
3. to loose blood
4. a small stream
5. to rest
6. to save
7. to look quickly
8. to try to find
9. hard, strong metal
10. to harden because of the cold
11. a plant that is not wanted

Page 59
A Sweet Smell

Valentine's Day is celebrated on February 14. The rose has been called the flower of romance and is often sent to another person on this day as a token of love.

Use the definitions to unscramble each word about flowers. Then, write the letter in each shaded box in order to answer the riddle below.

1. mtse — s t e m — the part that supports a flower
2. chunb — b u n c h — a group of flowers
3. lubb — b u l b — underground part from which some flowers grow
4. siyad — d a i s y — a type of flower with a yellow center
5. atlep — p e t a l — colorful part of a flower
6. erso — r o s e — a flower with a thorny stem

What flower does most everyone have?

TULIPS

Page 60
Circling Earth

On February 20, 1962, John Glenn became the first American to orbit the Earth. He circled the Earth three times during this historic flight.

To learn the name of Glenn's spacecraft, complete each analogy. The bolded boxes will spell the name of the spacecraft.

1. Pencil is to write as k n i f e is to cut.
2. Split is to divide as o r b i t is to circle.
3. Difficult is to hard as s i m p l e is to easy.
4. Ink is to pen as l e a d is to pencil.
5. Continent is to Asia as p l a n e t is to Earth.
6. Spelling is to letters as a d d i n g is to numbers.
7. Ocean is to whale as d e s e r t is to camel.
8. Sip is to drink as c h e w is to food.
9. Ankle is to foot as w r i s t is to hand.
10. Gallop is to horse as h o p is to frog.
11. 8 is to Kate as 7 is to Kevin.

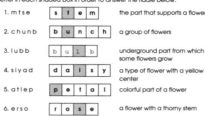

Page 61
The Birthday Bash

Presidents' Day is celebrated on the third Monday in February. Both George Washington and Abraham Lincoln were born during this month. Two other presidents were also born during February.

To find out their names, fit each word about George Washington and Abraham Lincoln into the puzzle. Start with the word or words with the most letters. Then, use the number code to write their names below.

George Washington		Abraham Lincoln	
federalist	first	Civil War	debates
general	Mount Vernon	Gettysburg	Kentucky
plantation	surveyor	lawyer	sixteenth
Virginia		stovepipe hat	

HARRISON and **REAGAN**

Page 62
A Bite of Health

Eating is one of the most important things we do every day. Nutrition is the study of how the food we eat keeps our bodies going. March is National Nutrition Month and a good time to learn more about nutrition.

Find the words about nutrition from the Word Bank in the puzzle. The words will go forward, backward, up, down, and diagonally. Then, write each remaining letter in order on the blanks below to learn an interesting fact about the body.

Word Bank

calcium
calorie
carbohydrates
energy
exercise
fats
fruit
iron
meat
milk
minerals
muscle
nutrition
protein
vegetable
vitamins
water

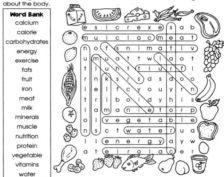

ABOUT TWO-THIRDS OF YOUR BODY IS ACTUALLY WATER!

Page 63
A Winning Woman

Women's History Month is celebrated in March to learn about the lives of important women. The first woman to win the Iditarod Trail Sled Dog Race in Alaska was Libby Riddles in 1985.

The racers in this race are called mushers. To learn more about Libby Riddles and the race, complete each word box using the sentence clues and the letter clues in the puzzle.

1. The race begins in the state of ____.
2. Ms. Riddles ____ books about the race.
3. The race ____ in Anchorage, Alaska.
4. Temperatures can reach 50 degrees ____ zero.
5. The Junior Iditarod is 150 miles for ____ racers.
6. The race begins on the first ____ in March.
7. The race is about 1,200 ____ long.
8. Each musher uses about 2,500 ____ of dog food during the race.
9. Mushers may start the race with 16 ____.
10. The ____ takes the mushers over rugged mountains.
11. This race is the ____ sled dog race in the world.
12. The ____ line is in Nome, Alaska.

1. A L a s k a
2. w r i t e s
3. B e g i n s
4. B e l o w
5. Y o u n g
6. S a t u R d a y
7. m i l e s
8. p o u n D s
9. D o g s
10. t r a i l
11. l o n g E s t
12. f i n i s h

Page 64
Sky Jumper

In March of 1912, Albert Berry made the first parachute jump from an airplane. The following year, Georgia "Tiny" Broadwick became the first woman to parachute from an airplane.

To find out how old Georgia Broadwick was when she made her first parachute jump, finish each word that begins with the letters *para*. Use the Letter Bank and the definitions as clues. Then, unscramble the circled letters to finish the sentence below.

Letter Bank

dise
graph
liel
mount
sol
ffin
lega
lyze
site

1. para L L E L : being the same distance apart at all points
2. para D I S E : a place of great happiness
3. para S O L : a small umbrella
4. para G R A P H : a group of sentences about the same idea
5. para F F I N : a white substance like wax
6. para M O U N T : above all others, very important
7. para L Y Z E : to take away the power to move
8. para L E G A L : a professional who assists a lawyer
9. para S I T E : an organism living in or on another organism

Tiny was **FIFTEEN** years old!

Page 65
Pig Punch Line

National Pig Day takes place during the first week of March. Other words for a pig are hog and swine. These words are synonyms.

Write a synonym for each clue. Then, use the number code to answer the riddle below.

lad — boy
ship — boat
human — person
writer — author
student — pupil
physician — doctor
teacher — instructor
infant — baby
bunny — rabbit
pony — horse
bug — insect

How do pigs write?

WITH A PIGPEN

Page 66
Phone a Friend

On March 10, 1876, Alexander Graham Bell spoke the first words over a telephone.

To find out what he said, write the homophone for each word. Then use the number code to complete the telephone message.

1. hare — h a i r
2. ewe — y o u
3. their — t h e r e
4. one — w o n
5. pain — p a n e
6. choose — c h e w s
7. meet — m e a t
8. know — n o
9. mail — m a l e

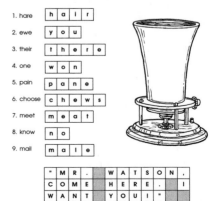

" M R .		W A T S O N ,
C O M E		H E R E .
W A N T		Y O U ! "

Page 67
Eight Useful Legs

March 14 is Save a Spider Day. There are more than 30,000 kinds of spiders. Because spiders eat harmful insects, they are helpful to people.

Use the definitions and letter clues to complete each spider puzzle.

S	e	a	r	c	h
o	P	e	n	e	d
t	h	i	r	t	y
s	a	d	D	l	e
r	a	c	k	E	t
e	r	a	s	e	R

1. to look for something
2. opposite of closed
3. ten less than forty
4. a seat on a horse
5. piece of equipment used in tennis
6. top of a pencil, used to remove marks

r	e	c	e	s	S
a	c	c	e	P	t
s	t	r	i	k	e
m	i	D	d	l	e
l	E	n	g	t	h
R	e	w	a	r	d

7. break time during school
8. to take something that is given
9. missing a pitch in baseball
10. halfway between two things
11. the distance from one end to the other end
12. a prize

Page 68
Try This!

A shamrock is the national symbol of Ireland. It has three leaves and is often worn on March 17, St. Patrick's Day.

Tri is a prefix that means "three." Use the grid to complete each word with the prefix *tri*. The first coordinate given is from the horizontal row of letters.

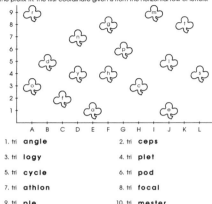

1. tri **angle**
2. tri **ceps**
3. tri **logy**
4. tri **plet**
5. tri **cycle**
6. tri **pod**
7. tri **athlon**
8. tri **focal**
9. tri **ple**
10. tri **mester**

Page 69
Sports Scoop

Did you know that a peach basket was used as the first basketball hoop? Learn more interesting facts during National Sports Trivia Week celebrated in the middle of March.

Which president played football for the University of Michigan? To find out, unscramble each sport. Then write the letter from each shaded box in order on the lines below to spell this president's name.

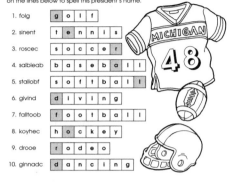

1. folg — g o l f
2. sinent — t e n n i s
3. roscec — s o c c e r
4. salbleab — b a s e b a l l
5. stallobf — s o f t b a l l
6. givind — d i v i n g
7. falltoob — f o o t b a l l
8. koyhec — h o c k e y
9. drooe — r o d e o
10. ginnadc — d a n c i n g

President **GERALD FORD**

Page 70
Time to Clean

March 20 or 21 marks the first day of spring. Traditionally, spring is a time for cleaning.

"Clean" each word by crossing out the letter that does not belong. Then, write the crossed-out letters in order on the blanks below to finish the fact about another popular spring activity.

1. eXxcited
2. picXnic
3. emergenXcy
4. tomatoX
5. reXceive
6. carroXt
7. volXunteer
8. greedXy
9. skinnXy
10. necXessary
11. fortXy
12. enouXgh
13. galloXn
14. learXn
15. imXprove
16. deXcimal
17. mammaXl
18. fXriend
19. nearXest
20. pleasXure
21. ourXselves
22. finalXy
23. leaXves
24. contXinue

KITES are the **OLDEST FORMS** of **AIRCRAFT**.

Page 71
A Number of Words

April is Mathematics Education Month.

Complete the crossword puzzle with mathematic vocabulary. Then, unscramble the shaded letters to answer the riddle below.

Across

1. a three-sided figure
4. repeated addition
6. no amount
8. the answer to an addition problem
9. Examples are 3, 5, and 7.
10. taking away one number from another
11. showing how many times one number contains another number

Down

1. ten times a hundred
2. Examples are 2, 4, and 6.
3. one thousand times one million
5. the distance around a figure
7. a part of a whole

Why was the math book unhappy?

It had too many **PROBLEMS**!

Page 72
Time to Fool

April 1 is April Fools' Day. On this day in France, a person tries to pin a paper fish on someone else's back without getting caught.

Oops! All the baby animals got mixed up. Use the code to write each baby's name. Then, draw a line to match it to its mother.

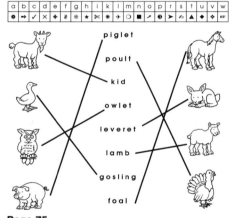

a	b	c	d	e	f	g	h	i	k	l	m	n	o	p	r	s	t	u	v	w

piglet
poult
kid
owlet
leveret
lamb
gosling
foal

Page 73
A Journey to the Top

On April 6, 1909, it is believed that Robert E. Peary became the first person to reach the North Pole. The *U.S.S. Nautilus* was the first submarine to travel under the Arctic ice to the pole.

Complete the puzzle using words that have to do with cold. Then, write the letter in each shaded box in order on the blanks below to learn Robert Peary's rank in the navy.

| i | c | e | c | r | e | a | m | s | l | e | d | m | a | m | m | a | l |

1. a frozen dessert made from milk products
2. carries people over the snow
3. a polar bear is this type of animal
4. a black-and-white bird that cannot fly
5. a sport played on ice wearing skates
6. a large piece of floating ice from a glacier
7. a hut built from blocks of snow
8. a heavy snowstorm
9. a hanging piece of pointed ice

ADMIRAL Robert E. Peary

Page 74
Space Flight

On April 12, 1961, Russian Yuri Gagarin became the first man to travel into space.

Man, space, and spacecraft are all nouns. Man is a person, space is a place, and spacecraft is a thing. Using the clues, write a noun that begins with each letter of Yuri Gagarin's name. To find out what Russian astronauts are called, use the number code to complete the following sentence.

Yuri Gagarin was a
COSMONAUT

Y	a	c	h	t
U	n	c	l	e
R	i	v	e	r
I	c	i	n	g
G	l	o	b	e
A	t	l	a	s
G	r	o	o	m
A	c	t	o	r
R	u	l	e	r
I	t	a	l	y
N	o	i	s	e

1. (thing) a large boat
2. (person) the brother of a father or mother
3. (place) a large stream of water
4. (thing) frosting
5. (thing) round ball with a map of the world
6. (thing) a reference book of maps
7. (person) a man getting married
8. (person) a performer
9. (thing) used to measure inches
10. (place) country in southern Europe
11. (thing) a loud sound

Page 75
Elephant Excitement

On April 13, 1796, America's first elephant arrived in New York. It came from Bengal, India.

Elephants are a popular attraction at zoos. Follow the other popular zoo animals listed through the maze. The letters go forward, backward, up, and down.

baboon
bald eagle
bactrian camel
chimpanzee
giant panda
giraffe
gorilla
hippopotamus
jaguar
king cobra
komodo dragon
leopard
llama
macaw
ostrich
penguin
polar bear
rhinoceros
sea lion
spider monkey
wallaby
zebra

Answers may vary.

Page 76
The British Are Coming!

On the evening of April 18, 1775, Paul Revere made his famous midnight ride to warn the colonists of the invading British troops.

Paul Revere's ride happened in the past. Fit the past tense of each verb into its puzzle. Then, use the number code to finish the sentence below about Paul Revere and his men.

1. feed
   ride
   sell

   r o d e (with s above, l below)
   f e d

2. hold
   make
   read

   m r / a e / d a / h e l d

3. bring
   build
   stand

   b u i l t (with s above)
   r o / o o / u o / g d / h / t

4. hang
   have
   win

   h a d / w o n / g

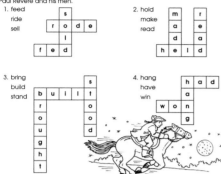

They were called **MINUTEMEN** because they had to be

ready to fight at a **MINUTE'S** notice.

Page 77
Huffing and Puffing

The first running of the Boston Marathon was held on April 19, 1897.

To find out how far this race is, complete each puzzle by writing a word that completes each sentence using the letter clue in the puzzle. Then, use the code to discover the answer.

A marathon is **TWENTY-SIX** miles long!

B e **h** i n d		The boy was hiding _____ the chair.
h O n e s t		Abraham Lincoln was a very _____ man.
a b **S** e n t		Because Kelly was ill, she was _____ from school.
g e n **T** l e		Please be very _____ with the kitten.
p o i **S** o n		A rattlesnake has _____ in its bite.
r e a s o **N**		Tell me the _____ you are late.

Mr. Rosman was elected _____ of our town.
There are _____ seconds in a minute.
I cannot _____ you to go until your work is finished.
Luis showed his _____ by stomping is feet.
Always look both way before you _____ the street.

M a y o r
s **i** x t y
a l **l** o w
a n g **E** r
c r o s s

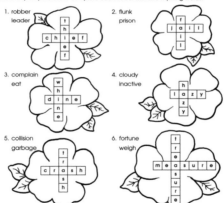

Page 78
Save Our Planet

April 22 is Earth Day. It is a day set aside for all to become aware of the need to preserve the environment.

Find each word in the Word Bank in the puzzle. The words go forward, backward, up, down, and diagonally. Then write the remaining letters on the blanks to find out when Earth Day began.

EARTH DAY WAS FIRST OBSERVED IN THE YEAR NINETEEN SEVENTY.

Word Bank
atmosphere
continent
crust
desert
glacier
inner core
mantle
minerals
mountain
ocean
outer core
plain
plateau
river
soil
valley
tributary

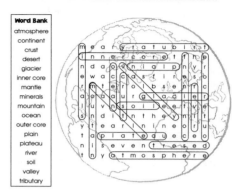

Page 79
Ways to Communicate

Samuel F. Morse was born on April 27, 1791. He invented the Morse Code, which changed the way people would communicate around the world.

Fill in each blank using the Morse Code to learn the year other communication inventions were invented.

| A | B | C | D | E | F | G | H | I | J |
| .- | -... | -.-. | -.. | . | ..-. | --. | .... | .. | .--- |

| K | L | M | N | O | P | Q | R | S | T |
| -.- | .-.. | -- | -. | --- | .--. | --.- | .-. | ... | - |

| U | V | W | X | Y | Z |
| ..- | ...- | .-- | -..- | -.-- | --.. |

1. 1867 **t y p e w r i t e r**
2. 1876 **t e l e p h o n e**
3. 1888 **b a l l p o i n t   p e n**
4. 1947 **t r a n s i s t o r**
5. 1965 **w o r d   p r o c e s s o r**
6. 1987 **l a p t o p   c o m p u t e r**
7. 1994 **d i g i t a l   c a m e r a**

Page 80
Rhyme Time

May Day is a spring festival celebrated on May 1. Often children dance around a maypole and hang baskets filled with candy and flowers on doorknobs.

Use the synonym clues to complete each flower with two rhyming words.

1. robber
   leader
   chief (thief)

2. flunk
   prison
   jail (fail)

3. complain
   eat
   whine / **dine**

4. cloudy
   inactive
   hazy / **lazy**

5. collision
   garbage
   crash / **trash**

6. fortune
   weigh
   treasure / **measure**

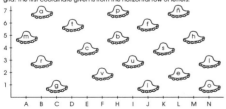

Page 81
Play It Again

National Music Week begins the first Sunday in May.

Fit the name of each musical instrument from the Music Bank in the puzzle. Use the letters m, u, s, i, and c as clues.

s a x o p h o n e
b a s s
o b o e
t r o m b o n e
g u i t a r
c l a r i n e t

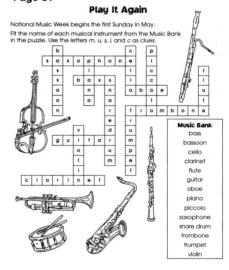

Music Bank
bass
bassoon
cello
clarinet
flute
guitar
oboe
piano
piccolo
saxophone
snare drum
trombone
trumpet
violin

Page 82
Festival Fun

Cinco de Mayo is a Mexican holiday celebrated on May 5. Many Americans also celebrate this holiday.

To find out more about Cinco de Mayo, complete each sentence using the grid. The first coordinate given is from the horizontal row of letters.

1. A Mexican festival is called a **f i e s t a**.
2. This holiday honors the **v i l l a g e r s** of the city of **P u e b l a** who fought the invading French army.
3. Children often play the **p i ñ a t a** game.
4. **M a r i a c h i** bands play music.
5. It is also a time to **f e a s t**. Many different foods are served including **t o r t i l l a s**.

Page 83
The Mighty Mississippi

In May of 1541, a group of explorers discovered the Mississippi River. They were searching for gold. Discover and search are action verbs.

Write an action verb in the puzzle for each sentence. The last letter of each word is the first letter of the next word. Some letters of the puzzle have been given. To discover the leader's name, use the code to fill in the blanks.

HERNANDO DE SOTO

l e a d
f
i
n
k n o w
r
i
e x p l o r e
a
t h r o w
a
t
c
h e l p
u
s
h i d e

1. Juan will _____ you to the treasure.
2. You should _____ water when you are thirsty.
3. I _____ the answer to the problem.
4. Tomorrow, Kristen will _____ Jack a letter.
5. We must _____ the entire cave.
6. The family will _____ dinner at six o'clock.
7. Lisa, please _____ me the ball.
8. We will _____ the movie again tomorrow.
9. Trent will _____ his dad rake the leaves.
10. Jill will _____ the grocery cart for her mom.
11. Sam likes to _____ behind the sofa.

Page 84
A World of Moms

Mother's Day is celebrated on the second Sunday in May. President Woodrow Wilson made this a national celebration on May 9, 1914.

Use the picture code to write *mother* in many different languages.

Czech	t a m a t k a
Dutch	d e m o e d e r
French	l a m è r è
German	d i e m u t t e r
Greek	μ α τ α
Italian	l a m a d r e
Japanese	(picture code)
Spanish	m a d r e

Picture Code
a
d
e
è
i
k
l
m
o
r
t
u
μ
α
ι
τ

Page 85

A Sour Treat

International Pickle Week is celebrated in the middle of May. Pickles are made from cucumbers.

To answer the riddle below, complete each analogy with a word that ends in *le* using the letter clues. Then, use the picture code to fill in the blanks below.

1. Geese is to goose as **c a t t l e** is to cow.
2. Drop is to baseball as **f u m b l e** is to football.
3. Horse is to stable as **c a s t l e** is to knight.
4. Aunt is to woman as **u n c l e** is to man.
5. Front is to forward as **m i d d l e** is to center.
6. Party is to friend as **b a t t l e** is to enemy.
7. Boring is to thrilling as **t e r r i b l e** is to wonderful.
8. Basket is to kitten as **c r a d l e** is to baby.

What is a crazy pickle?

A DAFFYDILL!

Page 86

Clara Barton

On May 21, 1881, the American Red Cross was formed. Its first president was Clara Barton. Clara Barton helped hundreds of soldiers during the Civil War.

To find out what Clara Barton was called, circle each word from the Word Bank in the puzzle. The words will go forward, backward, up, down, and diagonally. Then, write the remaining letters in order on the blanks below.

Word Bank			
ambitious	author	brave	courageous
fearless	generous	heroic	intelligent
lecturer	nurse	president	teacher

CLARA BARTON WAS KNOWN AS THE ANGEL OF THE BATTLEFIELD.

Page 87

A Day for Remembering

Memorial Day is observed on the last Monday in May. It was originally a day to honor those who died in the Civil War. Today this holiday also honors all who have died in any war while serving the United States.

To find out another name for Memorial Day, write the antonym for each word using the letter clue. Then, use the number code to write the letters on the blanks below.

C	h	e	a	p	expensive
d	i	r	t	y	clean
s	a	v	e	s	spends
b	e	g	i	n	finish
s	m	a	l	l	large

W	o	n	lost
	r	a w	cooked
	f	a r	near

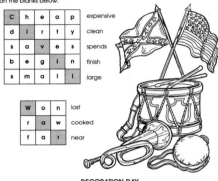

DECORATION DAY

Page 88

Hail a Cab

On May 31, 1907, the first taxis went into service.

To find out what city these cabs came to, unscramble each word. Each word has the letters C, A, and B in it. Use the pictures in the box as clues. Then, use the number code to write the city on the blanks below.

1. cabr — **c r a b**
2. cabno — **b a c o n**
3. cabynol — **b a l c o n y**
4. cabni — **c a b i n**
5. cabydrak — **b a c k y a r d**
6. cabontrutis — **s u b t r a c t i o n**
7. cabhe — **b e a c h**
8. cabrawdk — **b a c k w a r d**

NEW YORK CITY

Page 89

Rolling Down the River

June is American Rivers Month. The place where a river begins is the source of the river. The place where a river empties into another body of water is the mouth of the river.

Start at the source of the puzzle. Follow the names of American rivers listed in the River Bank to the mouth of the puzzle. The names of the rivers will go forward, backward, up, and down.

River Bank
Arkansas
Colorado
Hudson
Mississippi
Missouri
Niagara
Ohio
Platte
Potomac
Rio Grande
Sacramento
Shenandoah
Snake
Suwannee
Tennessee
Yellowstone
Yukon
Wabash

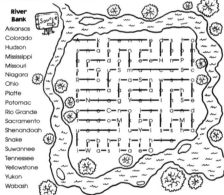

Page 90

Flying Proud

The first flag of the United States was adopted by the Continental Congress in 1777. This event is now celebrated as Flag Day on June 14.

To learn more about the flags of other places around the world, write the places from the Word Bank in the puzzle. Use the given letters *f, l, a,* and *g* as clues. After the puzzle is complete, write the name of the country below its flag on page 91.

Word Bank			
Australia	Denmark	Honduras	Scotland
Canada	France	Japan	Uruguay
Chile	Greece	Norway	
China	Greenland	Panama	

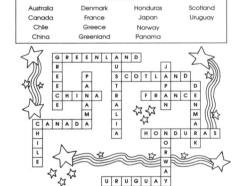

Page 91

Across

Greenland   Scotland   China

France   Canada   Honduras

Down

Uruguay   Greece   Australia

Japan   Panama   Denmark

Chile   Norway

Page 92

Summer Fun

Summer begins when the summer solstice occurs. This happens on June 20 or 21. On this day, there are more hours of daylight than any other day of the year.

Summer is a time for fun! Complete each sentence below with a word about summer. Then, find each word in the puzzle on page 93. The words will go forward, backward, up, down, and diagonally.

1. Grab your racket, and let's go play **t e n n i s**.
2. Mom packed a basket with food for our **p i c n i c**.
3. We are taking a **v a c a t i o n** to the Grand Canyon.
4. Carrie is riding her **b i c y c l e** to the park.
5. Mark hit a home run at the **b a s e b a l l** game.
6. We will cool off at the **s w i m m i n g** pool.
7. Summer begins in the month of **J u n e**.
8. On **J u l y** 4, there will be a celebration.
9. **A u g u s t** is the last full month of summer.
10. It is fun to spit seeds from a **w a t e r m e l o n**!
11. Ann picked a red juicy **s t r a w b e r r y** from the garden.
12. The Wilhelm family likes to **t r a v e l** to California during the summer.
13. We tried to catch a **f i r e f l y** last night.
14. There are no clouds, just lots of **s u n s h i n e**.

Page 93

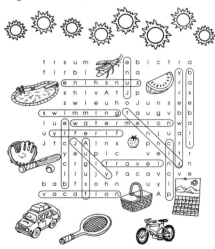

Page 94
A Perfect Pop

Father's Day is the third Sunday in June. A father has more than one job. Try to name all the things a father may do.

Many words have more than one meaning. Write the word that has the two given meanings. Then, use the number code to answer the riddle below.

1. to make a journey — `t r i p` — to cause someone to fall
2. a band around a finger — `r i n g` — a telephone sound
3. to go down below the surface — `s i n k` — a basin to hold water
4. to fasten — `s e a l` — a sea lion
5. a shape that has five points — `s t a r` — an actor who plays the leading role
6. to release — `f r e e` — no charge for something
7. bag for carrying things on your back — `p a c k` — to place in something for storing
8. to demonstrate — `s h o w` — a performance
9. the manager — `b o s s` — to give orders
10. hard growth on the head of some animals — `h o r n` — used to make a loud warning sound
11. to relax or sleep — `r e s t` — something that is left

Why did the golfer need two pairs of pants?

IN CASE HE GOT A HOLE IN ONE

Page 95
The Happiest Place

In July of 1955, Disneyland opened in California. Disneyland is known as "the happiest place on Earth."

Happiest is an adjective. It describes the noun "place." Using the definition clues, write an adjective that begins with each letter in Disneyland. Then, use the code to write the name of the city in which this park is located.

D	i	r	t	y	not clean
I	c	y			very slippery
S	m	a	l	l	tiny, little
N	e	a	t		well-kept, not messy
E	a	s	y		simple
Y	o	u	n	g	not old
L	a	z	y		not working hard
A	n	g	r	y	furious
N	i	n	t	h	after eighth
D	e	e	p		down far

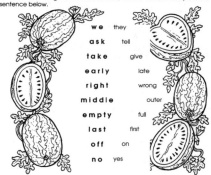

Disneyland is located in **ANAHEIM**, California.

Page 96
Light up the Sky

The United States celebrates its independence on July 4. Spectacular celebrations occur across the country.

Many other important events have also taken place on July 4. To learn about one of them, unscramble the words about this holiday. Use the pictures as clues. Then, use the number code to complete the sentence below.

1. tesbak — **basket**
2. dearap — **parade**
3. netarmewol — **watermelon**
4. daeelomn — **lemonade**
5. tLbiery elBl — **Liberty Bell**
6. deenneepcind — **independence**
7. charming danb — **marching band**
8. thourf — **fourth**
9. wrleforks — **fireworks**

On July 4, 1884, France presented this to the United States:
the **STATUE OF LIBERTY**

Page 97
Chip and Putt

July 18 is the anniversary of the first 18-hole golf course in America. It was built in Wheaton, Illinois in 1893.

Chip and putt are two actions a golfer does. Complete each puzzle with an action verb using the sentence clues.

c	o	m	b
c	h	o	p
s	a	i	l
s	k	i	p

1. Connor needs to _____ his hair.
2. I will _____ some wood for a fire.
3. The boat must _____ across the ocean.
4. The girls are going to hop, _____, and jump around the playground.

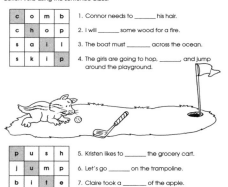

p	u	s	h
j	u	m	p
b	i	t	e
h	u	n	t

5. Kristen likes to _____ the grocery cart.
6. Let's go _____ on the trampoline.
7. Claire took a _____ of the apple.
8. Every night the cats _____ for mice.

Page 98
A Giant Leap

"That's one small step for a man, one giant leap for mankind." These are the famous words spoken by the first man to walk on the moon. This historic event happened on July 20, 1969.

To find out this man's name, use the definition clues and the words from the Word Bank to complete the path to the moon. Not all the words in the Word Bank will be used. Then, write the letters from each shaded box in order on the blanks below.

Word Bank
astronomy
crater
galaxy
gravity
Jupiter
Mars
Mercury
meteor
Neptune
Pluto
satellite
Saturn
universe
Uranus
Venus

1. the second farthest planet from the sun
2. the largest planet
3. the name for a group of stars
4. the science that deals with things in space
5. a mass of stone that comes from space
6. a body that orbits around another body
7. a hole in the surface of something
8. the farthest planet from the sun
9. includes everything in space
10. the force that pulls things toward Earth

NEIL ARMSTRONG

Page 99
Sweet and Juicy

August 3 is National Watermelon Day. Early explorers used watermelons as canteens.

To learn another interesting fact about this delicious fruit, write an antonym for each word using the letter clues. Then, use the code to complete the sentence below.

we — they
ask — tell
take — give
early — late
right — wrong
middle — outer
empty — full
last — first
off — on
no — yes

The **KALAHARI DESERT** is the birthplace of watermelon.

Page 100
Clowning Around

The first week of August is International Clown Week. Clowns have been around for hundreds of years. They have also been called jesters, buffoons, and Joeys.

Write two rhyming words with the same vowel sound as in clown for each definition.

1. a circular noise — **round sound**
2. a city dress — **town gown**
3. a yell of three strikes — **shout out**
4. a hurting sofa — **ouch couch**
5. a rodent's residence — **mouse house**
6. a pig's hit — **sow pow**
7. a discovered beagle — **found hound**
8. a sad part of speech — **frown noun**
9. white, fluffy noise — **cloud loud**
10. a right-away milking animal — **now cow**

Page 101
Blowing Its Top

Vesuvius is one of the world's most famous volcanoes. Its first recorded eruption occurred on August 24, 79 A.D.

To find out the country where this volcano is located, write a word for each definition using the letter clues. Then, use the code to write the country's name below.

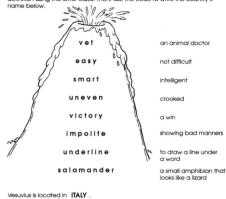

vet — an animal doctor
easy — not difficult
smart — intelligent
uneven — crooked
victory — a win
impolite — showing bad manners
underline — to draw a line under a word
salamander — a small amphibian that looks like a lizard

Vesuvius is located in **ITALY**.

Page 102
Popping Hot

Once the farmers in Missouri had something funny happen to them because it was so hot.

To find out what happened, unscramble each word which has the letters H, O, and T in it. Use each sentence as a clue. Then, use the number code to fill in the blanks below.

1. HOTLPSAI — Madison went to the **hospital** to get her tonsils out.
2. HOTLE — When my family went to Chicago, we stayed in a **hotel** with 22 floors.
3. HOTWR — Jason, **throw** me the ball.
4. HOTS — Susan **shot** the arrow at the target.
5. HOTUFR — Alex was the **fourth** person in line.
6. HOTMSTURREDN — The **thunderstorm** woke me up last night.
7. HOTCU — Do not **touch** the pan because it is very hot.
8. HOTOP — Kayla brought a **photo** of her dog to school.
9. HOTGU — That was a **tough** test!

CORN POPPED RIGHT OFF THE STALKS!

Page 103

Flying Fun

Did you know that scientists are trying to teach one kind of endangered bird to migrate from Wisconsin to Florida by dressing a scientist in a bird costume? Did you also know that another kind of bird can actually sleep while it is flying?

To find out what kind of bird each is, use the clues to name other things that fly. Then, use the number code to write each kind of bird in the boxes below.

1. This type of bird lives on every continent except Antarctica. It rhymes with "talk." — **hawk**

2. This person operates an aircraft. — **pilot**

3. This is what a group of birds is called. — **flock**

4. Although this black and white bird cannot fly in the air, it can "fly" underwater. — **penguin**

5. This insect, which is the color of grass, can leap about 20 times the length of its body. — **grasshopper**

6. This allows a person to jump from an airplane safely. — **parachute**

7. This beautiful, winged insect begins its life as an egg and then hatches into a caterpillar. — **butterfly**

An | a | l | b | a | t | r | o | s | s | can sleep while flying.

Scientists are teaching the | w | h | o | o | p | i | n | g | | c | r | a | n | e |

Page 104

What a Worm!

A blackbird in Britain hit the jackpot. It caught a very long worm.

To find out how long this worm was, use each definition clue to write a word with *or* in it. Then, use the number code to complete the fact below about worm's length.

f	o	r	t	a place with strong walls
s	o	r	e	a painful spot
s	c	o	r	e	the points in a game
s	h	o	r	t	not tall
d	o	c	t	o	r	a person who treats the sick or injured
b	o	r	i	n	g	not interesting
m	o	r	n	i	n	g	the first half of the day
e	x	p	l	o	r	e	to travel through newly found land
f	a	v	o	r	i	t	e	the one liked the best

The worm was **SIX FEET**,

FIVE INCHES long.

Page 105

Time for Bed

Do you know what can sleep in dry weather without waking up?

To find out, use the picture clues to complete each puzzle with two words about sleep. Then, use the code to complete the sentence below about the super sleeper.

d | r | e | a | m (with n, p below)

y | a | w | n (with s, t, r, s)

p | i | l | l | o | w (with a above)

q | u | i | e | t (with n, i, g, h, t)

b | l | a | n | k | e | t (with s, o, r, e below)

A **SNAIL** estivates, or sleeps, in dry weather until it rains.

Page 106

Too Cool!

Do you know why Hollywood film stars started wearing sunglasses?

To find out, find each "cool" word from the Word Bank in the puzzle. The words will go forward, backward, up, down, and diagonally. Then, write the unused letters in order on the blanks below.

Word Bank
admirable
applause
awesome
choice
dazzling
fabulous
famous
glamorous
groovy
hip
incredible
marvelous
sensational
smart

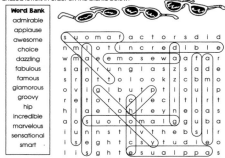

ACTORS DID NOT WEAR SUNGLASSES TO LOOK COOL BUT TO PROTECT THEIR EYES AGAINST THE BRIGHT STUDIO LIGHTS!

Page 107

Let Out a Shriek!

Gravity Road was the first roller coaster in the United States. It was eighteen miles long and was built in Pennsylvania to carry coal from a mountain to the canal below.

Finish each sentence with a word about a roller coaster ride to complete the puzzle. Use the letters in *Gravity Road* as clues.

s	t	r	a	i	g	h	t	s	c	r	e	a	m	(c, u, r, v)
k	d	r	o	p	f	a	s	t	s	p	e	e	d
c	a												
r	t	y	p	m	u	b	g	n	i	t	i	c	x	e

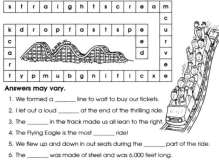

Answers may vary.

1. We formed a _____ line to wait to buy our tickets.

2. I let out a loud _____ at the end of the thrilling ride.

3. The _____ in the track made us all lean to the right.

4. The Flying Eagle is the most _____ ride!

5. We flew up and down in out seats during the _____ part of the ride.

6. The _____ was made of steel and was 6,000 feet long.

7. At the end of the ride, there was a long _____ straight down.

8. I cannot believe how _____ the roller coaster goes.

9. Sometimes the _____ is over 70 miles per hour.

Page 108

A Super Stretch

Who would not want to ride in a 100-foot limousine? This limousine was built in California, has 26 wheels, and is really incredible.

To find out what else this amazing limousine has, cross out the words that are not verbs in each box. Then, write the first letter of each word that can be a verb on the numbered blanks.

A SWIMMING POOL

1. arrow / ask / camel	2. study / stair / disk	3. now / glass / watch	4. itch / sooner / what
5. county / tomorrow / mail	6. awful / move / strange	7. imagine / above / word	8. success / nail / excellent
9. enough / rough / grew	10. ride / play / company	11. open / gentle / coarse	
12. those / grand / operate	13. year / laugh / behind		

Page 109

A Terrific Tongue

Did you know that a chameleon's tongue is often as long as its body? Its tongue shoots out so rapidly that a person can hardly see it!

Use this fascinating animal's name to complete each analogy.

1. Owl is to tree as king is to — c | a | s | t | l | e

2. Eyes are to see as teeth are to — c | h | e | w

3. Letters are to spell as numbers are to — a | d | d

4. Inner is to inside as center is to — m | i | d | d | l | e

5. Water is to ocean as sand is to — d | e | s | e | r | t

6. Leg is to knee as arm is to — e | l | b | o | w

7. Ending is to suffix as beginning is to — p | r | e | f | i | x

8. One is to single as two is to — d | o | u | b | l | e

9. Action is to verb as place is to — n | o | u | n

Page 110

Ouch!

One professional baseball player was hit by a pitch 267 times. This is a major league record.

To find out this baseball player's name, write each baseball word in the puzzle. Then, use the number code to write the name on the blanks below.

Word Bank
bunt
catcher
diamond
error
foul
outfield
pitcher
player
rookie
strike
umpire

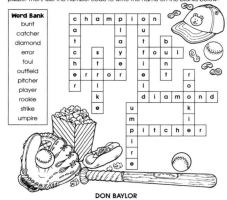

DON BAYLOR